O. Roger Anderson is Professor of Natural Sciences at Teachers College, Columbia University, and Senior Research Scientist at Columbia's Lamont-Doherty Observatory. He is Editor of the *Journal of Research on Science Teaching* and has also been a contributor to *Science Education*. His papers on pure science have appeared in the *Journal of Cell Biology*, the *Journal of Ultrastructure Research*, and the *Journal of Protozoology*.

TEACHING MODERN IDEAS OF BIOLOGY

O. Roger Anderson

Teachers College Press
Teachers College, Columbia University
New York and London

Library of Congress Catalogue Card Number: 73-185961

TEACHING MODERN IDEAS OF BIOLOGY is the first volume of *Studies in Science Education*, Willard J. Jacobson, general editor.

FOREWORD

In teaching, content and method are intricately intertwined. The most sophisticated methods are of little moment if there is nothing to teach. However, profound content can be lost, in fact negated, if the methods of teaching are haphazard and at variance with the nature of the content. Especially in science teaching, the nature of the discipline, science, may in part be communicated by the way we teach. For example, if we wish to develop a concern for evidence in support of statements, then we had better be concerned about evidence as we teach. If we wish to develop skills of enquiry, then we should demonstrate how we can enquire as we work with students. To ask, "Which is the more important, content or method?" is to ask an unuseful question. Both are important.

Since both content and method are essential, it seems logical that books on teaching science should deal with method within the context of content and discuss content in terms of method. This is not usually the case. Perhaps potential authors have hesitated because of the immensity of task—he who wishes to embark on such a book has to be sophisticated in both content and method. In this book, *Teaching Modern Ideas of Biology,* Professor Anderson has undertaken to discuss teaching, the psychological foundations of organizing ideas, and methods of analyzing the organization of classroom discourse within the context of the ideas of modern biology.

Effective teaching has definite objectives. Two kinds of objectives are suggested: outcome objectives and organizational objectives. Outcome objectives are stated in terms of anticipated changes in student behavior. An organizational objective is a statement of the kind of activity a teacher designs to achieve an outcome. It is suggested that this differentiation between the types of objectives will help a teacher to consider both the outcomes of a lesson and the organization of activities and discourse to achieve these outcomes.

Some fundamental concepts of learning psychology should be considered in organizing ideas for classroom presentation. Two categories of psychologies of learning are described: associationist and cognitive. Of special interest is the biopsychological theory of learning and communication which builds on the strengths of both the cognitive and associationist psychologies and is of interest and value to biology teachers. Of special importance is the grounding of the biopsychological theory on the concepts of biological evolution and psychological chaining. This may very well be the most sophisticated attempt to provide a biological base for understanding human communication and hence teaching. The biopsychological theory provides a framework for the unique method of analysis of classroom discourse that has been developed by Professor Anderson and is described in this book.

Eight lessons are described in considerable detail, each an example of a kind of lesson organization. For example, one lesson on Information-Carrying Molecules: The Nucleic Acids is a serial-centered lesson; as a contrast, the same lesson is developed as a cluster-centered lesson. Cell Membrane Structure and Function: A Search for Accurate Models is an example of an enquiry lesson on scientific model building, and Aquatic Life: Interactions among Living Things shows how a figural model can serve as a lesson theme. Following each lesson is an analysis of how it has been organized.

The sample lessons also provide an excellent summary of some of the modern ideas of biology. This kind of a summary is of special value to the biology teacher because it is directly linked to ways that biology can be taught.

The periodic analysis of the discourse that actually goes on in the classroom is of value to all teachers. Records of discourse can be made with a tape recorder. Professor Anderson describes effective ways of analyzing these records, using systems that have been developed for the analysis of structure in teaching. In this book there is a description of how the practicing teacher can use these analyses to improve his teaching.

Willard J. Jacobson

PREFACE

Within recent years the field of biology has undergone a remarkable transformation from descriptive science to dynamic investigation of the molecular and environmental factors influencing biological organization and activity. The new thrust toward a dynamic interpretation of biological phenomena has required an interdisciplinary approach that brings new unity to science as the various fields are applied to specific biological problems. New approaches to biological investigation require new patterns of teaching to complement diversity. Respectable strides have been made within recent years toward understanding basic principles of human learning and thinking. Although limited in scope and precision, this knowledge can be applied profitably to analyzing the organization of ideas to be presented in the classroom.

This book contains some practical suggestions for prospective and experienced science teachers who would like to know about principles of organizing content for effective communication and procedures for analyzing modern ideas of biology toward the improvement of science teaching. The first chapter sets forth a general rationale for the organization of biology lessons and pays specific attention to the classification of lesson objectives. Various principles of content organization are discussed in Chapter Two and illustrated in sample lessons presented in Chapter Three. Methods of analyzing lesson content organization are described in Chapter Four with some practical suggestions for improving one's own teaching through self-analysis. I hope that you find this book a useful guide in the daily practice of teaching and that it encourages you to think creatively about the organization of lessons on modern topics in biology.

O. Roger Anderson

CONTENTS

CHARTS

FIGURES

Chapter One

OBJECTIVES IN MODERN BIOLOGY TEACHING

The diversity of living things and the rich variety of concepts and principles we have created to describe this diversity provide a remarkable opportunity to teach biology in creative and divergent ways. The very complexity of this rich array of ideas can pose a problem in organizing them for their most effective presentation. Some orderly system is needed whereby the teacher can conceptualize and interrelate scientific ideas in flexible yet meaningful ways. Many creative and effective lessons can be prepared from intuition and spontaneously generated combinations of ideas. The new teacher who brings fresh insight to old problems and the mature teacher who has perfected some ways of dealing with these problems each has a source of rich experience to guide them in making intuitive decisions about lesson organization. When, however, spontaneous ideas are slow-coming, as is sometimes the case during the press of daily teaching, it is helpful to have some conceptual schemes as guides to flexible yet systematic lesson organization. Such content organization should be psychologically sound, and logically consistent with the structure of the discipline as the scholar has come to understand it. In this book we explore some principles of lesson planning, pupil learning, and content structure which suggest ways in which ideas can be ordered for effective classroom presentation. The ideas presented here are not intended to be exhaustive solutions to the problems of content organization, nor do they merit adoption to the exclusion of alternate ways of thinking about lesson planning. Hopefully, they will serve as a guide in stimulating your interest in finding new ways of composing effective and creative science lessons.

In this chapter the problem of defining instructional objectives is examined from a general educational viewpoint and specifically in relation to biological education. We begin with a discussion of the purposes of lesson planning.

When preparing to teach, one must decide how much of the classroom experience will be predetermined. Not all experiences in the classroom can be predetermined; some occur spontaneously as a result of the complex factors attending human interaction and the momentary interests of the participants. The alert teacher wants to allow sufficient freedom in the classroom to encourage responsible pupil planning and control of classroom activities when the occasion warrants it. However, an equally obvious fact is that there must be clearly established instructional purposes for the learning activities if the teacher and pupils are to be unified in their efforts. The process of defining purposes and anticipated outcomes of teaching is called objective setting. An objective is an aim or purpose to be accomplished during a learning experience. A well stated objective (one that makes explicit the anticipated experiences and their learning outcomes) not only guides classroom learning toward some purposeful end, but also serves as a criterion at the end of the lesson to determine how effectively the anticipated outcomes were achieved. A clearly stated objective is one that allows measurement of observable changes in human behavior. We shall have more to say about this at a later point.

In this book, we divide instructional objectives into two categories: (1) outcome objectives and (2) organizational objectives. An outcome objective is a statement of anticipated changes in pupil behavior as produced by classroom experiences. An organizational objective is a statement of the kind of classroom experiences one intends to use to achieve an outcome. In effect, we are making a distinction between product objectives and process objectives. In classical examples of classroom planning, objectives are frequently stated as pupil outcomes and the organization of classroom activities is treated as a separate category under a list of activities or projects. There is value, however, in treating instructional objectives as both outcome and organizational objectives. So doing allows the teacher to think deliberately and logically about the purposes of a lesson both as an organization of experiences and as outcomes the lesson is expected to produce. Moreover, by clearly separating and comparing the two kinds of instructional objectives (organizational and outcome), the teacher can think creatively about divergent ways of achieving outcome objectives through unique patterns of content organization and classroom activities. To further clarify the distinction between outcome and organizational objectives, some examples of each kind are given.

Sample outcome objectives:

1. The pupils will be able to state three hypotheses of DNA replication (conservative, semi-conservative, and dispersive).
2. The pupils will be able to list the steps in protein biosynthesis including messenger RNA production, soluble RNA activation, amino acid activation, amino-acyl linkage to soluble RNA, ribosomal participation in assembly of amino-acyl nucleotides on the messenger RNA template, and peptide bond formation.
3. When given a graph of cell culture growth showing a sigmoid relationship between cell number and time, the pupil will be able to explain the changes in the culture medium producing the curve.
4. The pupils will acquire skills in extrapolation of data from trends and sequences in photosynthetic processes.

The first three objectives are stated in behavioral terms. They define outcomes as directly observable behaviors which are used as evidence of covert gains in knowledge or cognitive skills. The fourth is a general objective. It defines the kind of cognitive gains one anticipates without specifying what operational evidence will be used to assess the gain. A general objective states a global aim. It is most useful as an intermediate step in objective setting. It is a way of getting a conceptual grasp of what will be accomplished by the lesson. Behavioral objectives can often be written more readily when preceded by a conceptual statement.

Sample organizational objectives:

1. The concept of ecological succession are presented as an integrating theme for teaching specific facts about plant and abiotic environmental interactions.
2. The concepts of natural selection and adaptation are explained to the pupils who then examine preserved plants and synthesize an explanation of their phylogenetic origin using the aforementioned concepts.

These two statements qualify as objectives since they state what is to be accomplished in the classroom. They are classified as organizational objectives since they define the kinds of instructional activities to be used. They are not outcome objectives since they do not define expected changes in pupil behavior. In most cases, however, an organizational objective states what the pupil does during a learning experience.

Classification of Instructional Objectives

- I Outcome Objectives
  - A. Cognitive
    - 1. Knowledge
    - 2. Skills
  - B. Affective
- II Organizational Objectives
  - A. Task
    - 1. Reception
    - 2. Discussion
    - 3. Operation
  - B. Content
    - 1. Structure
      - a. Serial-centered
      - b. Cluster-centered

2. Substance dimensions
   a. Specifics to generalities
   b. Structures to processes
   c. Constants to variables

In lesson planning, the teacher needs to give careful attention to the content of organizational objectives to be certain that it most effectively meets the intent of the outcome objective it is designed to support. Obviously, it is fallacious to define an outcome objective as acquisition of cognitive skills when the organizational objective for the lesson proposes a lecture on specific facts. This book is intended as an aid to good definition of objectives and means of flexibly and creatively planning lesson organization to achieve a wide range of outcome objectives.

Outcome Objectives

Outcome objectives are classified as cognitive when they concern the reception, storage, or mental manipulation of information. Knowledge includes acquisition and retention of information; skills concern the mental operations whereby knowledge is transformed in some orderly way. Affective outcome objectives concern student emotional responses to what is being learned. These include receptivity toward, sensitivity to, and acceptance or rejection of classroom experiences.

Knowledge and skill outcome objectives can be defined in behavioral terms or in general terms. R. F. Mager defines a behavioral objective as a statement of observable pupil outcomes. A behavioral objective should contain only those outcomes that are immediately reducible to measurable quantities. The statement "students will gain knowledge of scientific processes" is not a behavioral objective. According to Mager, no two people can agree on what constitutes knowledge. To "know" can encompass so many things as to make it virtually undefinable in specific terms. Therefore, to be specific from the outset, Mager recommends specification of the behavioral evidence one will accept for knowledge acquisition. Acceptable behavioral words expressing evidence of knowledge are "students will *list,* or *rank,* or *recognize in a list,* or *draw,* or *label.*" Behavioral objectives allow precise definition of expected cognitive outcomes and also are useful in test construction since they state exactly what the student is to do.

Although we recognize the value of behavioral objectives, we also give attention to the use of general objectives as well. There is strength in preparing lessons based on general and specific objectives. A general objective provides a conceptual view of what the teacher intends to accomplish. Within a framework of general objectives, one can draw out specific behavioral objectives. The general objectives allow flexibility in planning. They can be very helpful when spontaneous events in the classroom, such as a student question, suggest a different approach to teaching than proposed in the behavioral statement. With a general objective in mind, the teacher can reorganize his priorities and adjust his teaching method to meet the students' immediate needs and still achieve the overall objective of the lesson. We therefore give considerable attention in this book to defining general objectives as guides in lesson planning and recommend writing behavioral objectives as specific statements of anticipated outcomes. Hopefully, the discussions of organizing lessons presented here will help the teacher recognize how flexible planning based on general and specific objectives allows greater creativity and teacher responsiveness in meeting individual pupil and group needs.

Bloom and co-workers have produced a carefully systematized taxonomy of educational objectives for the cognitive domain. Their publication should be read for a thorough understanding of the kinds of general objectives that can be used in lesson planning. A summary of their classification of knowledge and skill objectives is presented here:

1. Knowledge: of specific facts, processes, principles, concepts, and theories
2. Comprehension: translation of information from one form into another, such as mathematical graphs or formulas

into verbal forms; interpretation of data—summarizing or presenting a central idea; and extrapolation of trends and sequences—extending trends in graphs or inferring end points of processes from intermediate data

3. Application: using principles, procedures, or theories in concrete situations, such as solving a problem by applying a rule
4. Analysis: of elements—identifying the components of a communication such as hypotheses in a theory; of relationships—identifying the interactions between parts of a communication, such as identifying predator-prey relationships; of organizational principles—recognizing systems or conventions for organizing information, such as the format of a formal scientific paper or the steps used in a laboratory procedure
5. Synthesis: production of a plan, or proposed set of operations, or derivation of a set of abstract relationships, such as designing a laboratory experiment or proposing a micro-theory to explain a set of laboratory observations
6. Evaluation: quantitive and qualitative judgments are made by application of criteria—assessing the value of a theory by examining how accurately it predicts laboratory data

Each category is listed with examples of the kinds of content to be taught.

1. Knowledge: specific facts. The kinds of chemical bonds stabilizing biological molecules, that is, van der Waals, ionic, hydrogen bonds, and covalent bonds; the structure of organelles in a generalized animal cell; the major classes of plants and animals in the taxonomic classification of living things; the root, stem, and leaf structure of hydrophytic, mesophytic, and xerophytic plants

   Knowledge: processes. Biosynthetic pathways in hemoglobin synthesis in mammalian red blood cells; development of the human embryo from egg to birth; cumulative

effects of water pollution on fish population in the Great Lakes
Knowledge: principles. Feedback control in enzyme systems; osmotic regulation of root pressure in plant cells; hormonal regulation of reproductive cycles; variation in animal phenotypes as a function of gene recombination during sexual reproduction
Knowledge: concepts and theories. One gene—one enzyme theory of nucleic acid control of enzyme biosynthesis; mitochondrial function theories of the nineteenth and twentieth centuries; origin of modern plants from more primitive kinds based on Darwinian evolution theory with citation of monophyletic and polyphyletic interpretations

2. Comprehension: translation. Of an electrocardiogram into a verbal explanation; of a graph relating O_2 production by elodea to photointensity of incident light; a verbal explanation of the hyperbolic Michaelis-Menten curve relating rate of enzyme action to substrate concentration
Comprehension: interpretation. The central concept of biogenesis in Pasteur's experiment using goose neck flasks filled with boiled beef broth; Malthus' concept of food limitation on population size obtained from reading one of his essays
Comprehension: extrapolation. Prediction of sugar translocation rates in plant stems as a function of temperature using the initial slope of the graph as a predictor; prediction of genotypes in the F_2 generation based on the parental genotype (P_1); interpolation of possible intermediate plant forms in the evolution of flowering plants from ferns
3. Application: of statistical chi square analysis to determine the significance of differences in phenotypes obtained by breeding fruit flies; plant classification into gymnosperms and angiosperms based on their stem anatomy and flower structure; preparation of an axenic protozoan culture using microbiological culture techniques
4. Analysis: of elements. Identification of the nephridia in

several cross-sections through the body of an earthworm; identification of the hypothesis in Pasteur's study of biogenesis using goose neck flasks; identification of classes of blood cells in a Wright-stained blood smear

Analysis: of relationships. Organization of stele and cortex tissues in plant stem cross sections; relationship of primary producers and secondary consumers in a fresh water food chain; relationships of nutritional dependence between sporophyte and gametophyte generations in plants from liverworts to flowering plants

Analysis: of organizational principles. Identification of design in Went's experiment on auxin regulation of coleoptile bending by removal of the coleoptile tip and its replacement at various positions; organizational patterns among woody plants, herbaceous plants, and algae in a climax deciduous forest

5. Synthesis: a proposal for an experiment to determine the effects of glycolic acid on the lag phase of algal culture growth; a plan to test the effects of certain drugs on visual conditioned responses in white mice and web building behavior in spiders as a means of testing a hypothesis that the drugs impair visual perception and motor activity; a design for a laboratory apparatus to maintain standing cultures of algae
6. Evaluation: an assessment of the effectiveness of antibiotics in producing bacteriostasis using inoculated agar plates and antibiotic discs; a critical review of an experiment on photosynthesis in chlorella to determine how effectively the experiment was controlled and how efficient were the methods

Organizational Objectives

Organizational objectives include the tasks proposed for completion by the class. These are reception learning (receiving verbal and visual presentations of the teacher or class members), discussion, and operation (manipulation of materials as in the laboratory). The second component of organizational objectives is the content to be presented. Two categories are defined: content structure (plan of organization), and substance dimension (kinds of content to be used).

The kind of task the teacher uses in organizing a lesson depends in part on the maturity of the student, the abstractness of the content to be presented, the limitations in organization imposed by the content itself, and the needs of the student to receive knowledge or gain skills.

Reception Tasks

Reception tasks presume the student receives information with minimum overt participation. The major part of the time is devoted to lecture, demonstration, or visual presentations by the teacher or a student leader. It is obvious that knowledge can be transmitted more efficiently by reception tasks than by discussion and operation tasks. One point of view often overlooked by teachers is that reception learning need not be a mere "pouring of facts and principles from one person's head into another's." A well organized lecture or demonstration can by its organization illustrate cognitive and laboratory skills. The well organized teacher who has acquired a clear understanding of Bloom's aforementioned taxonomy of cognitive skills in terms of science content can illustrate the processes for the pupils.

For example, a scientific experiment can be described in some detail. The theoretical assumptions underlying the experiment can be set forth. The process of analyzing previous data, extrapolating trends and sequences, evaluating the significance of prior findings, and deducing an experimental hypothesis can be illustrated in the teacher's presentation. Thus, the processes used in a scientific investigation can be made explicit by a careful discussion of the logical organization of the experiment, the laboratory methods used, and the kinds of conclusions drawn from the data. A critical analysis of the validity of the conclusions relative to the supporting data should be made. It is of obvious value to cite the names of cognitive processes used, so students come to recognize the mental operations as processes they can emulate.

Naive students who have had little formalized experience in cognitive skill training benefit most from such a reception task (of hearing about various ways of thinking) prior to their own practice of the mental processes. When planning reception tasks, the teacher clearly needs to keep in mind that such presentations can produce highly compulsive knowledge acquisition unless care is taken to provide many different examples of the content being presented and to suggest as many unanswered questions as is reasonable when describing scientific investigations. We have more to say about these organization parameters in Chapter Two. The general thrust of our present discussion is to emphasize the flexible use of reception tasks and to recognize that their excessive use can be very unstimulating and even boring to the middle school and high school student. Excessive use of lecture should be avoided when other tasks are available. Wherever possible, the teacher should plan to ask questions intended to arouse student responses demonstrating various cognitive skills. Such overt student responding during reception learning is a useful means of maintaining student involvement and gives the teacher feedback about how well the central knowledge or skill objectives are being met. If, of course, the dialogue is extended and students take more initiative in guiding the organization and content of the dialogue, the task becomes one of discussion.

Discussion Tasks

Classroom dialogue among most or all members of the group is classified as a discussion when there is no prescribed speaker dominating discourse. There may be a group leader who coordinates and moderates the discussion. The plan, however, is for all to participate in sharing ideas and summarizing pertinent knowledge required for problem-solving tasks. A simple problem-solving discussion task is presented in Appendix D.

Discussion tasks should be planned frequently for science classrooms. Science teachers have been, unfortunately, more reluctant than their colleagues in languages and social studies to adopt discussion techniques. Planning a discussion task requires careful selection of the topic to be discussed. In some cases students should be allowed to identify a problem area. It is wise to select topics that are suitable for analysis and evaluation. Current scientific controversy about a theory or model or about technological use of scientific information is often a source of ideas stimulating to group discussion.

A discussion task should be a planned dialogue on a topic about which the group members have made some preparation, either by reading or by performing laboratory investigation. It is wise for the teacher to allow part of the class to investigate one aspect of the problem and to require that results of the investigation be communicated to the other members of the class, thus establishing a basis for discussion. Small groups of students can be assigned the task of researching the topic of their choice. After preparing a review of its particular topic, each group should appoint a reporter to present the material to the class for discussion. It is important that each group clearly understands its role in preparing a report—namely, that the report should set forth the scientific data surrounding the controversy and then clearly pose one or more central questions to be discussed. An alternative scheme is to have one group assume responsibility for the background data on a scientific controversy and the remaining groups each prepare a position paper to be presented for class discussion. The teacher should be ready to allow student leadership to develop in the discussion, to provide suggestions when necessary for possible experiments that could be performed or possible cognitive skills that could be applied toward understanding the phenomena more fully, and to keep the group oriented toward the objective. Some attention should be given by the teacher or group leader to maintaining a flexible mental set among group members, welcoming, and where possible discussing, all reasonable contributions of diverse examples and possible solutions proposed by group members.

Operation Tasks

Laboratory time in secondary schools has traditionally been devoted to observation and description tasks. The laboratory is often seen as an extension of the formal lecture session where the student performs individual observations to confirm facts and principles stated by the teacher. Increasingly, we have come to recognize that the student should have an opportunity not only to observe data in the laboratory but also to formulate and test hypotheses, carefully consider the identification and control of variables in small laboratory projects, and generally to become aware of the various processes used by the scientist in purposeful laboratory investigations. The laboratory provides an excellent opportunity for the student to practice cognitive skills as well as manual laboratory techniques. The alert teacher plans for diverse laboratory experiences allowing analytical, evaluative, and synthesis skills. The student may plan during discussion sessions experiments to be completed in the laboratory. Small groups can be organized to perform parts of the analyses and data pooled for the next discussion session. Above all, the laboratory should allow the student enough autonomy to follow up creative ideas, and should at the same time be sufficiently well organized to prevent cognitive and physical chaos. Sometimes the teacher will want to allow the student complete freedom to guide his own enquiry, thereby allowing the student to understand the frustrations as well as achievements of scientific investigations. At other times, when the student needs advice (as we all do in research laboratories at one time or another), the teacher should provide a minimum of direction to keep the student oriented. Too much frustration reduces the student's confidence to further pursue scientific enquiry tasks and may jade his perception of the course. The general direction of modern biology laboratory exercises is toward greater emphasis on enquiry or open-ended experience and minimal use of mere observation laboratory sessions. These should, however, be used when the student needs preparatory information for further laboratory enquiry or elects to make observations in support of a long term project being undertaken by the group.

Content Structure

We will consider two ways of organizing content structure: serial-centered and cluster-centered. In a serial-centered organization of content, information is presented in small steps where each unit of information is carefully planned to flow logically into the next unit. The major emphasis is on the sequential organization of knowledge and skills. Maximum use is made of linking ideas of successive units in the sequence and earlier experiences are organized to maximally facilitate acquisition of later experiences. A cluster-centered organization places major emphasis on multiple relationships among substantive areas in the lesson. Rather than presenting content in small sequential steps, information is grouped into larger units wherein several characteristics (sometimes of diverse kind) are discussed. This organization lends itself to discussion of similarities and differences among concepts. Several different examples of one concept or principle may be interrelated by pointing out the characteristics common to all of them, and citing the characteristics not found in the examples as a way of clearly differentiating the concept from others in the same area. The cluster-centered organization in teaching allows greater flexibility in combining ideas and bringing divergent content materials within a common context thereby facilitating creative student thinking and stimulating classroom discussion.

The basic distinction between serial-centered and cluster-centered organization is that serial-centered lessons proceed by carefully integrated sequences of small idea units, whereas cluster-centered lessons emphasize the combination of diverse content categories into larger idea units with attention to comparisons and contrasts among the content categories and the simultaneous exploration of interrelationships among the categories by performing analyses and evaluations of the material.

Of course, a lesson can be organized to be partially serial-centered and partially cluster-centered. The purposes of the lesson in terms of outcome objectives and kind of content chosen suggest what mixture of the two kinds seem most appropriate. To further define the characteristics of serial-centered and cluster-centered lessons, some examples of each kind are given. The examples are in the form of outlines of lesson segments. For purposes of simplicity, we assume each segment is intended to teach knowledge of nucleic acid structure. The outcome objective for this lesson segment is knowledge of facts.

1. The structure of nitrogenous bases (pyrimidines and purines)
2. The structure of ribose (sugar) molecules and their covalent linkage to bases to form nucleosides
3. The ester linkage of phosphate molecules to the fifth carbon of a nucleoside to form a nucleotide
4. The phosphodiester linkage of nucleotides to form polynucleotides
5. The base-pairing of two polynucleotides to form a DNA double helix

In this example, the five major units in the lesson segment are arranged in a sequence such that each unit is logically related to the preceding one through common content. Moreover, subsequent units subsume earlier units thereby generating a hierarchy. An outline of a cluster-centered lesson segment on nucleic acids follows.

1. A general definition of nucleic acids: the characteristics of various forms of nucleic acids are set forth in a generalized statement.
2. The various kinds of nucleic acids are cited: nuclear DNA, mitochondrial DNA, chloroplast DNA, messenger RNA, soluble RNA, and ribosomal RNA.
3. The differences and similarities in structure of each kind are presented.
4. The structure of each kind is discussed in relation to its function.

In the cluster-centered lesson outline on nucleic acids, several ideas are continuously intermixed as the communication unfolds. Attention is constantly focused on the general relationships in structure among different kinds of nucleic acids. The distinction, therefore, between serial-centered and cluster-centered lessons is a matter of degree rather than kind. It is the degree to which content is developed in small sequential units as opposed to continuous intermixing of the ideas as the lesson unfolds. On the average, students find the cluster-centered lesson more difficult than the serial-centered lesson. The former requires greater cognitive strain in attending to the diverse characteristics being presented whereas the latter presents each small idea in easily consumable units. The close linkage of ideas between units helps the student associate the ideas without excessive cognitive expenditure.

The theoretical principles underlying the use of each kind of structure and the relative merits of each one in teaching are presented in Chapters Two and Three.

Substance Dimensions

Three substance dimensions have been identified according to their polar categories: (1) specifics-generalities, (2) structures-processes, and (3) variables-constants. Each dimension suggests a way of organizing content which is orthogonal to the other two. Although each dimension is independent—fully capable of assuming all values independently—their combination is completely compatible. This allows diverse combinations to be produced. The specifics-generalities dimension suggests opposing ways of organizing content. Content presented as specifics is very narrowly categorized and restricted to one or a few instances out of the total possible group of instances that could be considered. Generalities by contrast represent an inclusive and broadly categorized set of instances. For example, one can teach the concept of heart by discussing only four-chambered hearts as found in man. This constitutes a very specific presentation of the information. If, on the other hand, one discusses the heart as a generalized animal organ, encompassing examples from simple invertebrate animals through the mammals, the presentation is a general categorization since a very inclusive set of exemplars has been presented. As another example, the process of phosphorylation (ATP production) can be presented as a specific process occurring in an animal cell mitochondrion, or it can be discussed as a more general process occurring in all known forms of living cells including those in bacteria and photosynthetic plants. The process of photosynthesis can be taught as a specific set of reactions occurring in the chloroplast of flowering plants perhaps as cited for elodea (a very specific instance) or it can be presented more generally as a basic energy trapping process occurring in all photosynthetic organisms (a most general sense). The concept of natural selection can be taught in a very general way by citing its role in the evolution of varied forms of living things or it can be taught in a specific way by explaining the survival of various colored moths in a forest whose tree trunks have been blackened by soot.

One may assert intuitively that the optimal method is to present content in its most general form to increase transfer of training to new situations and maximize retention of the broad principles so engendered. Although this may be true as an ultimate objective in a lesson, we may sometimes want to begin at a more specific level before progressing to more inclusive categories. It should be apparent that this dimension of specifics-generalities allows presentation of content in either a very restricted context or in a more general form. Sometimes, as explained in Chapter Two, we may want to present content in the most general form and then move to specifics. In this light, the specifics-generalities dimension is a useful guide.

The second dimension is one of structures to processes. This continuum allows decision making about the kind of content to be presented. Structures are static representations of phenomena. These include all naturally occurring structures (cellular, tissue, organ, organismic, and community). Any descriptive category would be classified as a "structure" with reference to this dimension. The structures category also includes logical structures used to explain relationships among phenomena. These are classificatory schemes, categories, and models of interactions among living things or their component parts. Processes are time-correlated events and form the farthest pole of this structure-process continuum. A process is defined here as any sequence of connected events. Chemical pathways, growth sequences, ecological series (such as successions), evolution, nest-making, courtship behaviors, and life cycles are all processes.

To make clear the distinction between structures and processes, some examples of each are given. The four-chambered heart can be described as a structure by citing each component of the heart such as atria, ventricles, valves, coronary artery, and aorta. Only the names and spatial relationships of the components are given. The heart may be described as a process by stating the various changes that occur during a heart beat. Thus, the successive stages of contraction of the heart, the role of the relatively thin-walled atria in receiving the venous blood and emptying it into the ventricles, and the contraction of the massive ventricle muscles to force the blood into the arteries are described. The presentation of processes can be made more sophisticated by including a discussion of the role of the bundle of *His* in regulating heart contraction and electrophysiological processes accompanying contraction as represented by electrocardiograms. Again, a mathematical model to predict the number of organisms in a given environmental niche is considered a model of a structure since there are no process components. On the other hand, a mathematical model predicting the fluctuation in population numbers as a function of predator-prey interactions is a model of a process. The difference, thus, between structures and processes is that between static entities and dynamic events.

The constants-variables dimension concerns the regularity of occurrence of a phenomenon among various biological categories over time. For example, if one is discussing the chloroplast as a structure in green plants, a general model in which the chloroplast is treated as a constant type appearing in all forms of green plants can be presented. If, however, one chooses to differentiate among various kinds of chloroplasts in green plants by citing variations in structure, such as differences in grana structure, pyrenoid structure, and chlorophyll content, then the chloroplast is presented as variable. (Indeed, the chloroplast varies to the point of non-occurrence in some blue-green algae.) The constants-variables dimension, therefore, is a third kind of decision-making continuum used in defining instructional objectives. It is clearly different from the specifics-generalities dimension, and the distinction should be carefully maintained in one's planning. The specifics to generalities dimension considers the range of categories to be discussed in a lesson. Categories that are very few or highly particular constitute specificity. On the other hand, if the range of categories to be discussed is very broad and inclusive of many specific instances, this is a case of generality. The constants to variables dimension considers the regularity of occurrence of a phenomenon in relation either to a specific instance or to the most inclusive group. If the content is presented as occurring in every instance or continuously throughout time, it is a constant. Citation of variations in structure or discontinuity in appearance over time constitutes evidence of variability. One should always bear in mind that any structure or process presented without allusion to variations is considered a constant. In other words, it is tacitly assumed that a phenomenon is a constant unless explicitly described otherwise. This is one reason why a teacher should give considerable thought to this dimension in lesson planning. How much of what is presented should be clearly specified as a variable and how much should remain undifferentiated and hence acquired by the pupil as a constant?

To further illustrate the differences between the constants-variables dimension and the specifics-generalities dimension, an example is given. A function of the pancreas in a broad group of mammals (generalization) is the synthesis of insulin for regulation of carbohydrate metabolism. This can be presented as a constant if no further qualifications are made. However, if one chooses to describe diabetes mellitis as a disease accompanying loss of pancreatic synthesis of insulin, one describes an instance of variability since insulin production is not a constant characteristic in all animals. The reader should not have great difficulty in grasping the concept of the constants-variables dimension since it is simply a matter of presenting data as an unalterable, ubiquitous occurrence among the categories being discussed or as a variable occurrence.

To facilitate lesson planning with reference to all three dimensions, they are combined into a three dimensional model in Figure 1. Each content dimension is presented as an axis on the model. The vertical axis contains the specifics-generalities dimension, the horizontal axis within the plane of the paper contains the structures-processes dimension, and the remaining axis, projecting into the plane of the page and at right angles to the structure-processes axis, is the constants-variables dimension. Four cells occur above the horizontal plane defined by the structure-process

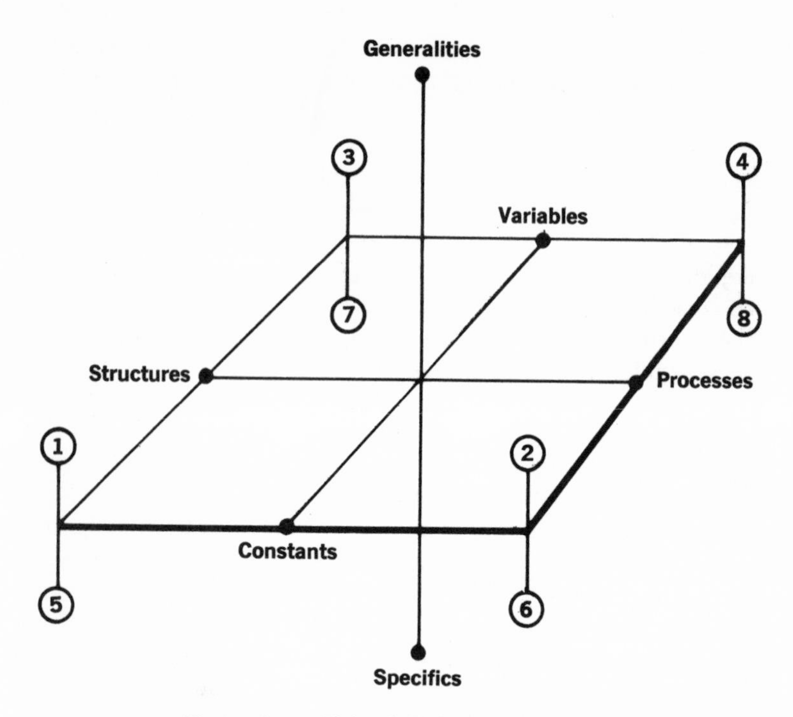

Figure 1 Eight Cell Coordinate Model
Four cells above the horizontal plane (cells 1 through 4) contain generalities as a common characteristic. Four cells below the horizontal plane (cells 5 through 8) contain specifics as a common characteristic. Each of the eight cells contains a particular combination of categories represented by the three axes.

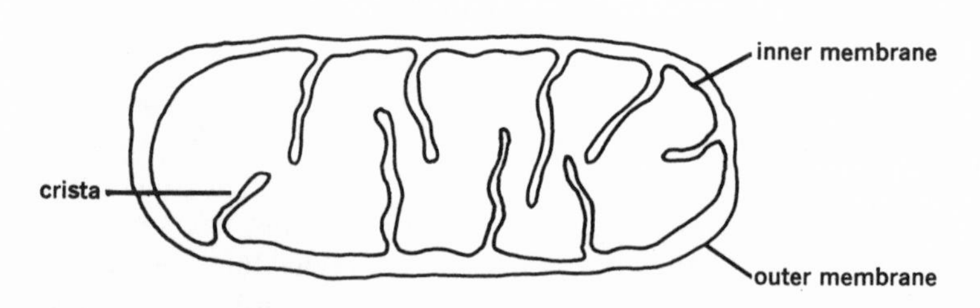

Figure 2 Model of a Mitochondrion

and the constant-variable axes, and four occur below the plane. The eight cells are numbered consecutively from left to right and front to back as shown in Figure 1. The characteristics of each cell relative to the graph's axes are:

Cell	*Content*
1	Constants, structures, generalities
2	Constants, processes, generalities
3	Variables, structures, generalities
4	Variables, processes, generalities
5	Constants, structures, specifics
6	Constants, processes, specifics
7	Variables, structures, specifics
8	Variables, processes, specifics

Examples of content organized according to a plan for each of the eight cells in the model follow. The content is mitochondrial structure and function. The organizational principles illustrated with this limited topic can of course be applied to more elaborate topics. An outline of the content in each cell is presented. The italicized word in each heading is the major variable being changed relative to the preceding examples. Only one or two dimension variables are altered at each step in the series of examples. The diagram in Figure 2 can be used as a figural reference for each example.

Cell 1: Constants, *structures,* generalities

1. Mitochondria are cellular organelles surrounded by a double membrane.
2. The outer membrane forms an envelope enclosing an inner membrane which is convoluted, forming sac-like protrusions into the, central intra-mitochondrial space.
3. The inner membrane protrusions are called cristae.
4. The cristae contain knob-like projections from their surfaces, whereas the outer membrane is smooth.
5. Mitochondria are found in most living cells including protozoa, plants, and invertebrate and vertebrate animals.
6. One function of mitochondria is to produce the energy-rich molecule called ATP to maintain cellular metabolism.

7. ATP is a universal energy storage molecule used by most living things to maintain life and facilitate growth.
8. Several electron micrographs of mitochondria from diverse tissue in many different organisms should be displayed for the students.

Cell 2: Constants, *processes*, generalities

1. The mitochondrion is a cellular organelle whose major function is production of energy-rich molecules called ATP.
2. ATP is produced by the break down of sugar molecules through several steps.
3. In the first step sugar molecules (containing 6 carbon atoms) are broken down to form 3-carbon-atom molecules. Some ATP is produced here.
4. The 3-carbon molecules enter the Krebs cycle in which they are broken down to yield hydrogen-carrying molecules.
5. The hydrogen-carrying molecules enter a final respiratory chain where oxygen is eventually consumed and ATP is again produced.
6. The mitochondrion contains an outer smooth membrane forming a globose sac, and an inner folded membrane with small knob-like projections.
7. The outer membrane may be the site where sugar is broken down to 3-carbon-atom molecules.
8. The inner membrane is the site at which ATP is produced by energy transfer and uptake of oxygen.
9. Most animal and plant cells produce ATP by mitochondrial processes.

Cell 3: *Variables, structures,* generalities

1. Mitochondria are cellular organelles surrounded by a double membrane.
2. The outer membrane forms an envelope surrounding an inner membrane which is convoluted thus forming sac-like protrusions into the central intra-mitochondrial space.
3. The inner membrane folds are called cristae.
4. The structure of the crista varies depending on the kind of cell. Mammalian cells often have flattened sac-like

cristae resembling hot water bottles. Cristae of protozoan mitochondria, however, are sometimes tubular, forming finger-like projections.

5. The cristae contain knob-like structures on their surfaces.
6. One function of mitochondria is to produce energy-rich molecules called ATP.
7. Most living cells in a wide range of organisms contain mitochondria. Bacteria and some yeast cells do not have mitochondria. Thus we see that the structure and presence of mitochondria vary among different cells.

Cell 4: Variables, *processes*, generalities

1. The mitochondrion is a cellular organelle whose major function is production of energy-rich molecules called ATP.
2. ATP is produced by the breakdown of sugar molecules through several steps (the same steps as cited in cell 2).
3. Although most cells produce ATP, some do not have mitochondria. The process of ATP production in bacteria where there are no mitochondria apparently occurs on cytoplasmic membranes. Some yeasts do not undergo respiration and only the first step of sugar breakdown to 3-carbon-atom molecules is used in ATP production.
4. You will also need to know that molecules other than ATP are used as high energy storage molecules. These are GTP, UTP, CTP, and TTP. However, of all of these ATP is the most widely utilized as a source of energy for a variety of cellular processes.

Cell 5: Constants, structures, *specifics*

1. The mitochondrion of the mammalian liver cell is typical of animal mitochondria.
2. It contains an outer membrane forming a globoidal sac surrounding an inner membrane composed of numerous surface folds projecting into the intra-mitochondrial space.
3. The cristae of the liver cell mitochondrion are flattened pocket-like structures containing small globose projections on the inner surface.
4. One function of the mitochondrion is to produce energy-

rich molecules called ATP which support metbolic processes in the liver cells. Some examples of liver functions are blood detoxification, storage of glycogen, and bile production.

Cell 6: Constants, *processes*, specifics

This example is substantially the same as that reported for cell 2; the function of mitochondria in a specific cell or in a specific process such as fatty acid elongation should be presented.

Cell 7: *Variables, structures*, specifics

1. The yeast cell mitochondrion structure varies depending on the presence or absence of oxygen in the growth medium.
2. When yeast is grown in an oxygen-rich medium, the mitochondria are well developed. They display the typical outer sac-like smooth membrane surrounding an inner convoluted membrane containing surface granules.
3. When oxygen pressure is low, the yeast produces large quantities of alcohol and little oxygen is consumed. The mitochondria disappear.
4. Smooth membrane components remain as the site of ATP synthesis by glycolysis.
5. Thus, we see that in certain yeasts the structure of the mitochondrion changes and may disappear under oxygen-poor growth conditions.

Cell 8: Variables, *processes*, specifics

1. The yeast cell requires energy to grow and reproduce.
2. Energy for life processes is stored in a molecule called ATP.
3. Mitochondria are cellular organelles which produce ATP.
4. One step in ATP production is called glycolysis and does not require the presence of oxygen.
5. This step can be performed by smooth membranes in the yeast cell.
6. Another step in ATP production is respiration. This occurs in the mitochondrion where oxygen is consumed and energy is released to form ATP.

7. Both processes of glycolysis and respiration occur when oxygen is present.
8. When oxygen is absent, the yeast cell no longer is capable of respiration, sometimes mitochondria disappear, and only glycolysis produces ATP.
9. This process in yeast is called fermentation.

Various combinations of content dimensions can be used in conjunction with the structural categories (cluster-centered or serial-centered) in planning organizational objectives. These concepts allow an orderly yet flexible way of preparing content for classroom presentation.

The eight cell coordinate model moreover facilitates careful planning of lesson sequences. The sequential order of topics to be presented can be analyzed with reference to the parameters cited in the model (Figure 1). The teacher can make decisions about the content to presented at each point in a series of topics. For example, once the content to be presented has been identified and the teacher has assessed the pupil's needs and preparation for the lesson, a decision should be made about the lesson sequence.

Assume the teacher chooses to present a linear (serial) lesson. The question next arises as to what cell in the model best represents a starting point. For example, shall the lesson be initiated with a presentation of specific structures as constants in the biological system (cell 5), or should the lesson begin with a more general discussion of a process which occurs in all parts of the biological system without exception (cell 2)? Once this decision has been made, one must ask whether the whole lesson will follow this plan or whether it should lead into discussion based on a different combination of dimension factors. Perhaps the second part of the lesson sequence is highly general and dynamic in content, suggesting that cell 4 best represents this phase of the lesson. We see that proper sequential ordering of the lesson content can be planned by referring to the options available in the eight cell model. Practical examples of lesson sequences using the eight cell model as a guide are given in Chapter Three. These examples are more readily understood in relation to the principles of lesson organization presented in Chapter Two.

Organizational objectives should be defined in a context of the broader purposes of the lesson. The teacher may decide to organize a very open classroom experience to facilitate pupil initiative and objective setting. Under these conditions, the teacher as participant in classroom planning should be alert to cite the various content categories that can be pursued, thereby giving the pupils the widest possible range of categories for their choices. In reception learning, when the teacher is largely responsible for the content organization, the objectives of lesson planning should be defined to facilitate content acquisition in as flexible a way as possible. By flexible cognitive acquisition of content, I mean presenting content in as broad a context as possible. This implies that at some point in most lessons, the teacher will want to present content with maximum generality. This implies the use of cells 1 through 4. Particular value for flexibility of knowledge acquisition is indicated by use of cells 3 and 4 where major emphasis is on variability of biological phenomena at a high level of generality.

Generality as used in this model does not necessarily mean abstractness; rather, it means inclusiveness and comprehensiveness. When planning lessons, some attention should be given to the abstractness of material in addition to its generality. The proper balance between abstract and concrete materials should be determined for each group of pupils. High intelligence groups will no doubt require fewer concrete examples to acquire knowledge of an abstraction than low intelligence students.

Chapter Two

PRINCIPLES OF ORGANIZING IDEAS

Some fundamental concepts of learning psychology are presented here as a basis for a more detailed discussion of organizing ideas for classroom presentation.

Learning psychologists fall into two broad categories: (1) associationists and (2) cognitive psychologists. Associationists, because of their interest in single and sometimes small steps in learning have been called molecular psychologists. The cognitive group, which studies broader schemes of learning and is concerned with holistic mental representations of experience are called molar psychologists. The differences between these two groups are partly methodological. The molecularists study individual environmental events and specific responses aroused in the observer. Molar psychologists study the mental integration of several environmental events and attempt to generate field theories (cognitive maps) as explanations of human mental activity. Philosophical differences also exist at the level of explanation deemed sufficient to adequately understand human behavior. The associationists assume that a precise understanding of mental activity can be achieved only by a careful examination of the individual stimulus-response linkages which underly larger patterns of human behavior. Cognitive theorists on the other hand assume that human behavior is too complex to be reduced to fragmented stimulus-response connections particularly if one's objective is to know something about the complex mental activities that accompany classroom learning. They, therefore, aim to achieve a holistic view of human mental activity and build models of human behavior as an extended network of events variously described as cognitive frameworks, schemas, fields, or mental maps.

Each way of viewing human behavior has strengths as well as weaknesses. What the associationists gain in prediction of specific responses, they lose in their inability to predict larger patterns of cognition, such as problem solving and place learning (remembering spatial maps and positions of objects in space, for example). The cognitive theorist's power to build models representing larger behavior patterns is sometimes mitigated by the incapacity of their models to predict with precision individual human responses to specific environmental stimuli. The classroom teacher finds value in knowing something about each of these psychological views of human learning and using that knowledge as a frame of reference in interpreting classroom behavior and planning wisely the organization of classroom activities. By this admittedly eclectic approach, the weaknesses of each system are ameliorated by the strengths of its complementary kind.

There have been few successful attempts to create a middle-ground theory of human behavior which combines into one logically consistent model the values of the molecular and the molar views. A model of learning based on biological and psychological principles of human behavior which is of this middle-ground kind has some value in planning and analyzing the organization of human verbal learning (knowledge and cognitive skill acquisition). We consider in sequential order associationist models, cognitive models, and a biopsychological explanation of human learning. The merits and limitations of each model are discussed with the aim of helping classroom teachers apply each appropriately to their classroom practices. It is most important for the teacher to critically understand the limitations of each system. During classroom teaching, you will find that sometimes none of the models adequately explain the events, nor do they yield an optimum prediction of how the problem should be met. Under these circumstances, you need to refer to a philosophical position outside of psychology or rely upon intuition; to try innovative approaches of your own and evaluate their outcomes.

The value in knowing some psychological principles of learning is at least three-fold. First, many of the daily problems of planning lessons can be facilitated by a broad and enlightened view of how people learn. Second, psychological models of learning provide a frame of reference within which to create new approaches to teaching which can be integrated with previous psychological knowledge and efficiently shared with colleagues who also understand the language of psychology. Third, a knowledge of psychology allows one to reflect systematically and logically about classroom problems and to formulate rational decisions about ways of ameliorating them.

It is assumed throughout this book, moreover, that the teacher has acquired a critical understanding of psychological theory. Such an understanding includes recognizing the limitations as well as strengths of current psychological models. We attempt to build a critical understanding of some fundamental principles of learning theory.

Such a critical view, honestly recognizing the limitations of each model, allows for flexible application and greater freedom in choosing alternative models when the demands of the problem are not met.

Association Theories

Association theories of learning assume that the environment influences our behavior in predictable ways. The influences of the environment to which we are responsive are called stimuli. The reactions which one makes to a stimulus are called responses. This association of environmental influence and organismic reaction is called a stimulus-response connection or association. It is symbolized as S-R. The symbols are S (stimulus), dash (association), and R (response). The definition of a stimulus is any environmental event which produces a reaction in an organism. The range and kind of stimuli to which an organism is sensitive depend in part on the physiological state of the organism (its ability to sense the stimulus, for example) and the previous history of the organism in responding to stimuli identical to it or nearly so. Most associationists accept the idea that stimulus-response associations are strengthened with repeated arousal of the two. Many associationists assume that the strength of an association depends not only on its frequency but also on the effect which accompanies such an association. By strength of association we mean the probability of response arousal when a stimulus is presented. Thus, a stimulus which arouses a response only infrequently forms a weak association with the response, whereas a stimulus which arouses a response nearly every time the stimulus is presented forms a strong association with the response.

A reinforcer is any event which accompanies the S-R arousal and tends to increase the likelihood that the response is elicited by the stimulus in the future. Some associationists distinguish between primary reinforcers and secondary reinforcers. A primary reinforcer is any event that meets a basic animal need, usually a physiological need such as food, warmth, and security against harm. Secondary reinforcers include verbal statements and material tokens which have become symbols for the primary reinforcers. Statements of approval, a hand gesture signifying acceptance, or monetary gifts and remunerations are examples of secondary reinforcers. The most general definition of a reinforcer is any event which strengthens an association. This highly empirical view looks for no mechanical explanation of the strengthening effect. It merely recognizes that any event which increases the probability of a response following a stimulus is by observation of its effect a reinforcer.

Associationist theories vary as to the necessity and time order of the occurrence of reinforcers. Guthrie (Hilgard and Bower, 1966) proposed a theory of stimulus-response contiguity which assumed that reinforcement or effect is not necessary. He stated that responses become associated with stimuli when the two occur simultaneously or nearly so. Guthrie explains simple verbal learning of symbols and signs as such a contiguity event. A child who is induced to say *apple* when the object is presented comes to associate the word with the object through contiguous presentation. Thus, according to Guthrie, the simultaneous occurrence of the visual object (apple) and the child's pronunciation of the word *apple* is sufficient to account for the learning of the association.

Other associationists accept the necessity of a reinforcer but differ as to when the reinforcer is to occur. Those who follow a Pavlovian model assert that the reinforcer should precede or occur simultaneously with the response it is intended to reinforce. The Pavlovian conditioning paradigm is shown in Figure 3.

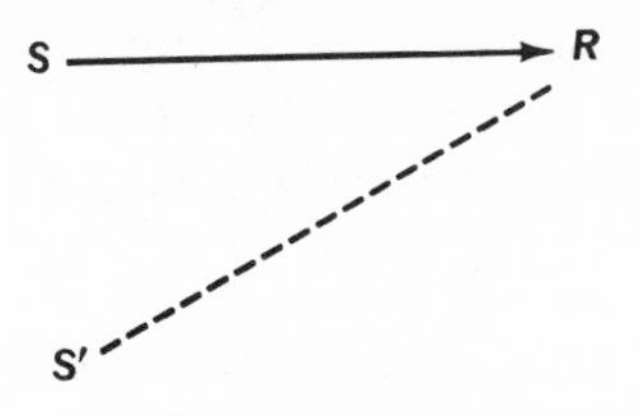

Figure 3 The Pavlovian Conditioning Paradigm

An event S is some influence which arouses a response *R*. This linkage may be a physiological reflex which occurs through genetic inheritance. In Pavlov's original experiments, the event S was meat powder placed on a dog's tongue. This influence excited taste receptors in the tongue, and effected salivation through a nervous system reflex response. The event S′ is a neutral stimulus which, prior to the conditioning situation, had no effect on the response *R*. In Pavlov's experiments, this stimulus was the well known ringing of a bell. By pairing the neutral stimulus S′ with the reflex stimulus S many times, the neutral stimulus becomes associated with the response and is then called a conditioned stimulus. The conditioned stimulus comes to arouse the response in the absence of the reinforcing reflex stimulus S. We are all familiar with Pavlov's demonstration of this effect. The sound of the bell, having been presented many times with the application of meat powder to the dog's tongue, eventually aroused salivation when presented alone. Thus, salivation became associated with the bell stimulus when meat powder was used as a reinforcer. Pavlov found of course that the bell-salivation association strength tended to decline unless an occasional presentation of meat powder accompanied the bell stimulus. Since the meat powder enhanced the strength of the bell-salivation association, it can rightly be called a reinforcer. In Pavlovian conditioning, the reinforcer precedes the response.

In recent times other associationists have recognized that reinforcers may also follow a response and increase its frequency of arousal. B. F. Skinner developed a highly empirical model of learning which emphasized among other things the role of consequences rather than antecedents during conditioning. Skinner described a paradigm known as operant conditioning. Unlike Pavlovian conditioning, operant conditioning assumes that a stimulus *following* a response will reinforce the response if the stimulus is a positive reinforcer. Operant conditioning is symbolized in Figure 4.

$$s \text{ - - - - - - - - - } R \longrightarrow S$$

Figure 4 Operant Conditioning Paradigm

According to Skinner, certain responses *R* are aroused by unknown (unspecified) general stimuli *s*. If a stimulus S is supplied following a response and the response occurs more frequently after each stimulus application, the stimulus is empirically determined to be a reinforcer for the response. Skinner makes an objective analysis of conditioning. He does not attempt to identify the many physiological conditions (*s*) that might arouse a particular response (*R*). Rather, he contrives a situation in which the particular response is likely to occur and then arranges to reinforce the response by applying following the response a stimulus such as food which might increase the frequency of the response. Skinner recognizes the existence of Pavlovian reflex conditioning as one kind of conditioning which he chooses to call respondent conditioning. One difference, therefore, between operant conditioning and respondent conditioning is that reinforcing stimuli follow the response in operant conditioning, whereas reinforcing stimuli precede the response in respondent conditioning.

Skinner's concept of operant conditioning is best understood by illustration of his experimental method. Skinner uses a device known as a Skinner box. Although there are many different kinds, one commonly used is illustrated in Figure 5. This is called a bar-pressing box. The lever at one end of the box is attached to an external food delivery mechanism which drops a pellet of food into the cup whenever the lever is depressed. Skinner puts a

Figure 5 Bar-Pressing Box

hungry albino rat into the box. Eventually during the animal's random search movements, it depresses the lever with its paw. Food is delivered almost immediately and the animal eats the pellet. The animal will soon again depress the bar and receive food.

Skinner found that frequency of bar pressing increased substantially when food was presented after the response. Eventually the animal became conditioned and pressed the bar repeatedly even when food was delivered only occasionally. This demonstrated Skinner's hypothesis that infrequently occurring responses can be strengthened by presenting a reinforcing stimulus following the response.

Thus far, we have examined only how operant conditioning results in increased frequency of responding. We next consider how an association can be produced between a response and an arousing stimulus. Skinner calls this process discriminative operant conditioning. To entrain a response to a particular external stimulus, the stimulus is presented only during those times when the response is being made and reinforced. Thus, the stimulus does not occur when the organism is performing responses which are not reinforced. The close temporal pairing of the external stimulus with a reinforced response gradually produces an association between the response and the stimulus as shown in the paradigm illustrated in Figure 6.

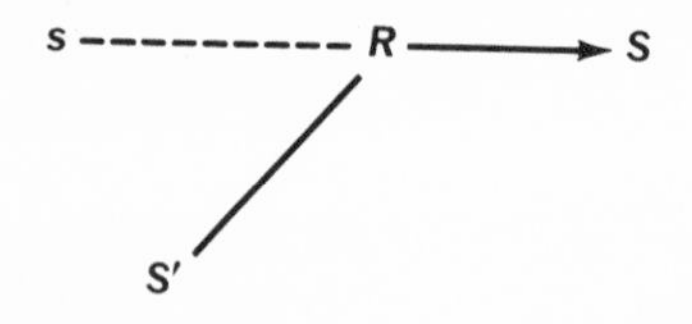

Figure 6 **Model of Discriminative Operant Conditioning**

The stimulus S′ is presented each time the operant response *R* occurs and is followed by a reinforcing stimulus S. Eventually, as a result of this specific pairing, the stimulus S′ comes to arouse the response *R*. The reinforcing stimulus S is applied occasionally to maintain the strength of the association. To fully develop the concept of discriminative operant conditioning, we apply the model to the aforementioned Skinner box.

Assume that the bar pressing box is equipped with a small white light above the bar in full view of the rat and that the experimenter has arranged for the light to go on each time the rat presses the bar and receives food. After several trials of bar pressing and light blinking, the rat becomes conditioned to the light as a discriminative stimulus. Presentation of the light alone arouses the bar pressing response. Food must be applied occasionally to maintain the strength of the association. Skinnerian theory of operant conditioning has found its greatest practical application in programmed instruction. This system, which has become widely recognized in professional practice, consists of a sequence of statements (stimulus items) and questions to be answered (responses). Upon completion of the response in the context of the stimulus question, the learner checks his response. The correct response appears in an answer space, reinforcing the learner's behavior if it was correct. This is a practical example of discriminative operant conditioning. The stimulus in the program statement corresponds to a discriminative stimulus which gives rise to a response. If the response is correct and hence reinforced, the association between the stimulus and the response is strengthened. Skinner emphasizes the value of correctly responding on the first trial. Thus programmed materials are written to maximize chances of correct responses which ensure immediate reinforcement of the response and also circumvent the deleterious effects of punishment which suppress responding when the student makes too many wrong responses. Moreover, Skinner recognized that a false response aroused by a discriminative stimulus gains some strength of association merely by occurring in its presence. Therefore to avoid reconditioning the pupil to respond properly to the stimulus, Skinner recommends careful organization of programmed stimulus items to ensure proper responses.

As a way of pointing out the empirical qualities of Skinner's operant model of conditioning, we briefly describe C. L. Hull's contrasting model of response reinforcement by drive reduction. Hull is an associationist who accepts the concept of reinforcement as part of his theory of learning. He assumes, however, that reinforcement need not be external and that internal physiological states (postulated to exist but not directly observable) provide a mechanism for response reinforcement. According to this theory, an organism experiences an internal state of arousal called drive. A drive state is a condition of the organism which causes it to be active. A drive as such has no direction, but merely stimulates the organism to action. Other factors, such as environmental cues, direct the behavior toward some goal. Hull postulates that the organism remains aroused and active until some response is made which reduces the drive state. The response which reduces drive is thus reinforced and likely to be repeated. Hull theorizes that organisms build up habits or predictable ways of responding to stimuli to reduce the drive aroused by the stimuli. According to his theory, there exists a habit hierarchy. This is a series of responses an organism is likely to make when presented with a stimulus. The response with greatest strength in the hierarchy is elicited first and then, if need be, the next most dominant one is aroused, and so on until the drive state is reduced or the hierarchy is exhausted. If the latter occurs, the organism responds by trial and error until some new response is produced which reduces drive. That response is accordingly reinforced. Hull's theory is particularly appealing as an explanation of learning under deprivation or in problem situations. Subjectively, his approach seems very reasonable. We all, no doubt, have sensed internal tension and lack of fulfillment when confronted with a problem situation. We also may realize a sense of release and fulfillment when a solution is found. The reduction of tension is introspectively a good example of Hull's sense of drive reduction. It is also equally reasonable that the solution to the problem that resulted in drive reduction will be used again if the problem arises at another time. Much of Hull's theory is intuitively reasonable. The concept of a habit hierarchy agrees well with observation of human behavior in the classroom. Pupils confronted with a problem frequently attempt several solutions beginning with ones which previously have proven successful. Sometimes old habits serve new ends and the problem is solved and the habit is reinforced by the reduction in drive aroused by the problem.

The weakness of Hull's system lies partially in its concept of drive. If learning is a product of drive mechanisms and their reduction—phenomena which cannot be observed or easily regulated in human beings in any predictable way—how can the teacher use this theory effectively? Moreover, the lack of empirical methods of controlling response arousal and reinforcement severely limits the use of this theory in predicting student behavior and planning meaningful learning exercises.

Skinner's theory of operant conditioning is appealing because it uses observable response reinforcement—namely application of an environmental stimulus to increase the response frequency. Moreover practical applications of the theory reveal methods of leading the pupils through sequences of small step exercises that provide the context for maximal correct responding and immediate reinforcement. Skinner's theory, moreover, has the salutary quality of emphasizing the value of positive reinforcers and maximizing success in learning rather than the using tension or avoidance concepts to control behavior. Skinner's approach shares the weaknesses of most associationist theories. It deals with small units of behavior and assumes that a response must be aroused overtly before associations can be made. It is this limited binary S-R association and stereotyped response acquisition that makes Skinner's theory less appealing for understanding problem solving and creative behavior than the models presented by cognitive psychologists.

Association theory has been expanded to better explain complex sequential behaviors. The concept of stimulus-response chaining allows such an expansion. According to chaining theory, sequential motor and verbal behavior can be explained as a series of responses which have become linked so that the arousal of one response initiates the arousal of a second until the whole series has been elicited. Arousal of one response in the chain serves as a discriminative stimulus for, and specifically arouses, the next response. The subsequent response acts as a reinforcer for the preceding arousing response, thereby strengthening the preceding response and linking the responses together. The net result of the combined discriminative stimulus-reinforcement function of each response in the sequence is to produce a closely linked, fairly stable chain of associations. This is illustrated in Figure 7.

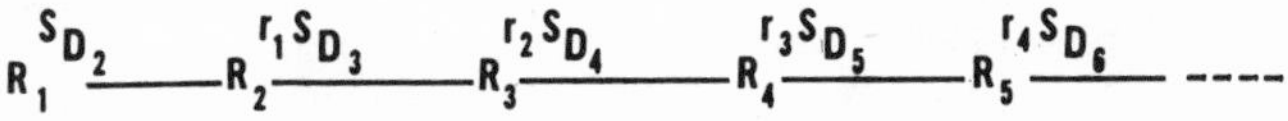

$$R_1 \overset{S_{D_2}}{\longrightarrow} R_2 \overset{r_1 S_{D_3}}{\longrightarrow} R_3 \overset{r_2 S_{D_4}}{\longrightarrow} R_4 \overset{r_3 S_{D_5}}{\longrightarrow} R_5 \overset{r_4 S_{D_6}}{\longrightarrow} \text{----}$$

Figure 7 A Response Chain Model

Five responses are shown in series. Each response has a dual function in the chain: it serves as a discriminative stimulus for the next response (SD) and as a reinforcer (r) for the previous response.

How is a chain of responses formed? The initial arousal of a chain of responses is achieved by presenting a carefully designed sequence of stimuli intended to elicit responses in serial order. If the responses so aroused have reinforcing properties for the preceding *response* and have stimulus functions for the succeeding response, the chain is established. The prompting stimuli are no longer necessary. Sometimes, of course, the prompting stimuli must be presented for several trials before the chain becomes established. Thereafter, only the initial response need be aroused to elicit the complete chain of responses. Figure 8 shows the role of prompting stimuli in forming a chain. The dashed lines linking prompting stimuli with their responses indicate that these stimuli are needed only during conditioning and become superfluous once the chain is established. The initial stimulus is, of course, necessary to arouse the first response and it is shown with a solid line linkage to its response. The reinforcing and stimulus properties of the responses for one another are shown by appropriate directed lines.

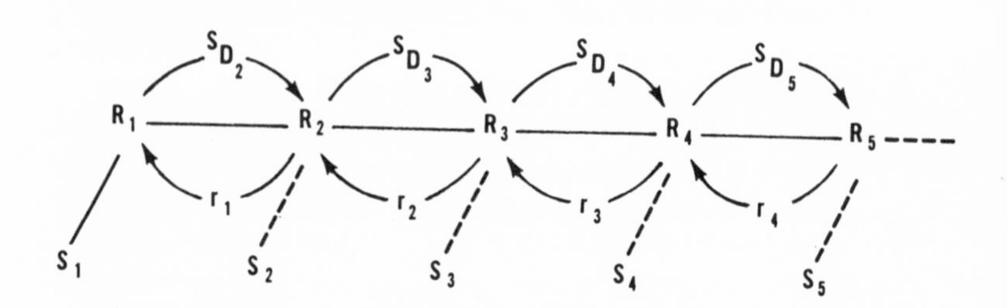

Figure 8 A Model of Chain Formation
The role of prompting stimuli (S) in forming a chain of responses (R) which becomes self-generating when the reinforcing and stimulus properties between the responses are established as shown by arrows. The prompting stimuli are no longer necessary to elicit the chain once the first response has been aroused.

This model has obvious value in explaining the long term remembering of complex serial information such as multiplication tables, verbal passages, and sequential mathematical and reasoning skills. The sequence is self generating and self reinforcing, and thus remarkably stable against perturbations. One of the merits of chaining theory is that it suggests certain practical strategies for efficient teaching of serial learning. If the objective of a lesson is to maximize acquisition of carefully ordered series of facts and skills, the following principles of teaching are recommended.

1. Arrange the materials to be learned in small units thereby minimizing pupil confusion about the proper response he

is to make and ensuring immediate reinforcement of each correct response.

2. Provide sufficient prompting cues when presenting the material that the learner will clearly perceive the principal response that is to be acquired. For example, make explicit the central idea or group of ideas or skill behavior to be acquired at each step.
3. Order the learning material in such a way that first presented material facilitates subsequent learning. Material presented early in a sequence should give a preview of subsequent material, or serve as introductory content to which material acquired later may be related in a more abstract or general way.
4. Each pair of responses acquired in series should be related to one another in such a way that the prior learned response is reinforced by the subsequent learned response. This means that the second response in a series pair should have some properties in common with the first response.

Efficient sequences of analysis, evaluation, and logical reasoning should be used in a context of as many different problems as possible. This increases the probability that the learner will be able to apply the skills in future problem solving situations since the chains of responses have been acquired in association with diverse cues. By this means, the generalization potential of the learned skills has been increased. Association theories of learning allow us to make predictions about the generality of stimuli associated with a response (the extent to which diverse stimuli will arouse a given response) or the discriminability of a response (its specific and isolated association with a limited group of stimuli). Stimulus generalization is the condition of having many stimuli to which a response or chain of responses is associated. In some cases, stimulus generalization is desirable as in teaching creative and flexible ways of thinking. We in fact would like the learner to acquire as broad a stimulus base as possible, to increase the range of situations wherein the response is validly applied. At other times in teaching, it is desirable to limit the range of stimuli to which a response is made. The student will sometimes need to differentiate among stimuli in order to avoid an erroneous response. For example, in teaching the concept of mammal, we obviously want to establish clearly what attributes of animals should be associated with the stimulus mammal, and which should not. Establishing a limited set of one or more stimuli to which a response is to be made is called differentiation.

The concepts of generalization and differentiation are useful in thinking about the organization of lessons. Their application to lesson planning allows a systematic determination of responses acquired with highly general associations and those acquired as more differentiated. Decisions made with regard to this dimension dictate, of course, the kind and range of examples used, the variations in problem situations to which the pupil is exposed, and the amount of time to be spent in developing specific knowledge within categories as opposed to time spent on broader, less well differentiated learning. In summary, the strength of association theory is its precision in explaining small step learning, serial learning, and individual response generalization and differentiation with regard to range of stimuli arousing the response. The limitation of this theory is its emphasis on particular learning rather than general patterns of learning and its limitation in explaining complex mental processes.

Cognitive Theories

We turn now to some models of learning based on cognitive theory and applicable to the practical problems of teaching examined in this book. We discuss specifically the work of David Ausubel, Robert Gagné, and Jerome Bruner.

Ausubel proposes a theory of meaningful verbal learning based on a concept of cognitive subsumption. Meaningful learning, according to Ausubel, is acquiring new knowledge through relating to existing knowledge. Rote learning consists of acquiring isolated responses that cannot be subsumed within the learner's existing cognitive framework. Nonsense learning, such as random collections of alphabet letters, is non-meaningful since the mate-

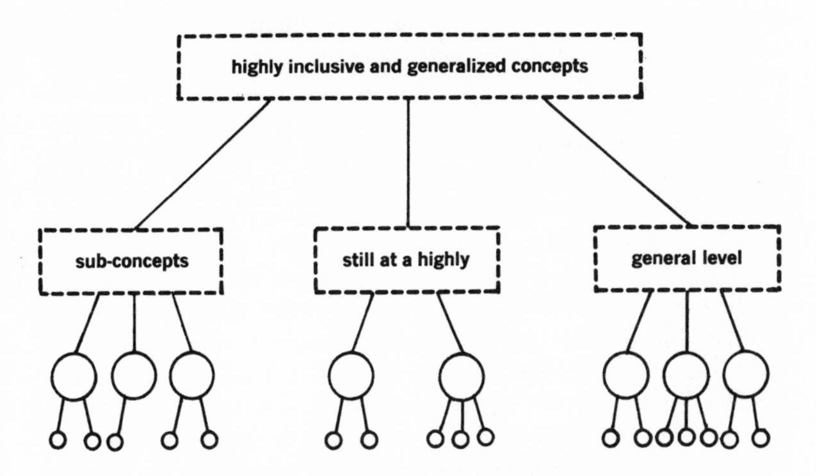

Figure 9 A Cognitive Hierarchy Proposed by Ausubel
Highly inclusive concepts subsume less inclusive sub-concepts which in turn provide anchorage for related specific ideas. The whole system forms an ideational scaffold with the generality of ideas increasing as one proceeds upward.

rial cannot be related to existing knowledge. Subsumption theory of learning is based on the premise that prior learning is the most significant factor in determining the ease and permanence of new knowledge acquisition. If the learner has acquired a set of abstractions and generalities which is stable, hierarchically organized, and highly inclusive, then he is likely able to relate new knowledge to existing cognitive categories and acquisition is enhanced. Ausubel speaks of an ideational scaffolding or cognitive structure as a body of interconnected principles and generalities. If this cognitive structure is highly stable and inclusive, providing easily mobilized foci to which new knowledge can be related, acquisition and retention possibilities are enhanced. Subsumption theory suggests that meaningful learning is an accretion process with new bits of knowledge being related to and subsumed by existing bodies of knowledge. We thus are led to conceive of cognitive structure as a hierarchical framework with highly general principles and concepts at the top subsuming more concrete and specific kinds of knowledge at lower levels. One of the functions of the teacher is to facilitate the student's acquisition of a stable, generalized, and inclusive set of abstractions to facilitate later acquisition of specifics.

Once such a cognitive system has been established, the teacher can cite the generalizations previously taught, thereby mobilizing the subsumers and making them available for association with specific ideas to be taught. Ausubel defines a generalized set of concepts capable of subsuming subsequently presented specific facts as an advance organizer. An advance organizer is a generalized ideational field presented prior to presentation of specific facts relevant to the field. According to Ausubel, the advance organizer mobilizes cognitive subsuming concepts which facilitate learning of related specifics.

This concept of an advance organizer may be understood readily from the following study (Ausubel, 1960). Undergraduates of matched reading ability were divided into two groups. One group was given a preliminary reading task on the similarities and differences between metals and alloys, their respective advantages and limitations, and the reasons for making and using alloys. This information was presented in a highly general and conceptual way without reference to specific material presented later. The other group of subjects was given a preliminary reading passage, but the content was a historical description of the field of metallurgy. The passage was found typically in introductory textbooks and provided few generalized concepts or abstractions that could serve as cognitive subsumers. The first group thus was prepared for an experimental reading passage on steel by reading an advance organizer on general concepts in metallurgy, whereas the second group read comparable advance material but of a specific and non-generalized kind. Three days after reading the advance material and the experimental passage on carbon steel, both groups were tested for knowledge of specific facts in the carbon steel passage. The group receiving the advance organizer achieved significantly greater knowledge acquisition scores than the control group. Ausubel concluded from his experiment that the group receiving the advance organizer retained more information than the control group because the advance organizer provided clearly distinct and appropriately relevant subsuming foci for anchorage of the specific facts acquired during reading of the carbon steel passage. The historical introduction provided few generalized concepts that could serve as anchor for specific facts acquired by reading the carbon steel passage. Therefore, the acquired ideas were more fugacious, less readily discriminated from previously learned material, and hence not retained efficiently. The significant gain in retention of the advance organizer group as compared to the historical group provided strong evidence in support of Ausubel's theory of facilitative acquisition of new knowledge through cognitive subsumption. According to subsumption theory, advance organizers enhance retention of specific ideas by providing stable and clearly delineated anchor points to which the specific ideas can be related. In the absence of an advance organizer, it is unlikely that newly acquired ideas will be subsumed by the most stable and relevant foci. Indeed, through cognitive reorganization, unstable associations may be broken, thus rendering the ideas unavailable to recall, or the ideas may be obliteratively subsumed by less relevant subsumers so that their meaning becomes obscure and recall inhibited. An advance organizer, therefore, serves at least two functions: (1) it enhances the meaningfulness of reception learning by providing relevant subsuming concepts to which new ideas can be related, and (2) it strengthens retention by providing a clearly delineated and stable set of foci for association of the ideas.

Ausubel's theory of cognitive subsumption is particularly useful in planning lesson sequences. To maximize clarity of acquisition and enhance retention of specific content, the teacher is advised to prepare an advance organizer to precede the presentation of the specific ideas. The advance organizer should contain highly general and inclusive concepts that will serve as anchor points for the specific facts. This means that the teacher should think carefully about the concepts and principles which are most likely to provide a framework to which the specifics can be related. Once such a set of concepts has been gathered, it should be organized into a concise overall description of the material to be learned. Thus, the advance organizer is an introductory statement which attempts to establish an overview of the main concepts that the teacher feels should serve as anchorage for the more specific ideas to follow. It is wise to consider carefully the prior learning of the students and relate the advance organizer to that learning by citing similarities and differences between the new concepts and already learned ones. It is also recommended to begin with the most general ideas and gradually introduce subconcepts at a less general level, thereby creating a clearly delineated hierarchy of abstract ideas in the advance organizer. By this sequential organization, the most approximate and immediately relevant subsuming concepts are available when the teacher begins presentation of specific facts.

For example, suppose that a teacher plans to give a lesson on animal nutrition. Some specific facts to be learned are about food used by various organisms to support life and the mechanisms by which food is produced or obtained. The lesson might contain a description of food-getting processes in various plants and animals beginning with the simplest unicellular organism and progressing through more advanced plants and animals, including eventually man. If these are the specific facts to be learned, the teacher needs to invent an advance organizer to introduce the lesson before proceeding into the main citation of specific food-getting mechanisms.

An advance organizer for this lesson could be built upon the concept of energy flow in the environment, as shown in the following paragraph:

Energy, the capacity to do work (as the students no doubt learned in general science), is essential for the maintenance of life. Movement, growth, reproduction, and health of all organisms depend on the presence of a source of energy. In our solar system the main source of energy is the sun. Plants generally receive solar energy as sunlight and use the energy to produce complex energy-rich molecules such as sugar and indirectly to produce proteins and fat. Moreover, green plants trap some of the sunlight energy in a lower energy form, as chemical molecules. In turn, animals feed upon the plants thereby securing the energy-rich molecules for the maintenance of their own bodies. Eventually the animals die and are decomposed by bacteria which thus use the same energy for their own growth and reproduction. In this general sequence, we have seen how energy flows from the sun into the environment on earth causing changes in the physical environment.

Upon the completion of the advance organizer, the teacher should have ready a definite plan for discussing the specific food-getting processes of living things. It is most logical to begin with the simplest green plants, algae, and explain their use of sunlight to synthesize food. From here the lesson could proceed through representative higher order green plants, briefly illustrating the same energy trapping processes as were cited in algae. Then, animals (heterotrophs) could be discussed, with specific examples of predators on algae and extending a short aquatic food chain. Finally, a food chain among terrestrial animals could be used to complete the lesson. Whenever possible, allusions should be made to the energy flow from prey to predator thereby mobilizing subsuming foci presented in the advance organizer. The merits of subsumption theory in teaching are: (1) it provides the teacher with a system for thinking about the effects of prior learning on the acquisition and retention of new ideas; (2) advance organizers are convenient tools to enhance the clarity and orderliness of lesson organization; and (3) the concept of a hierarchical organization of knowledge with general inclusive concepts subsuming less inclusive and more specific concepts provides a practical model of cognitive structure which the teacher can use to organize lessons. This suggests a sequence of progressive differentiation where more general concepts are presented first followed by increasingly specific material.

The limitations of the theory are, (1) that it explains only reception learning and does not easily explain higher order thought processes, and (2) that it is difficult to reduce some of the theoretical constructs to clearly representative concrete and practical terms. For example, can one precisely identify in practical or operational terms what constitutes an ideational framework or ideas with a high degree of generality and inclusiveness? As with many cognitive theories, the gain in generality of the theory and its capacity to explain global patterns of learning are often achieved at the expense of precision in identifying exemplars of the theoretical constructs.

Gagné has studied hierarchical learning and proposed a model of sequential learning particularly useful in organizing lessons on principle learning and acquisition of problem-solving skills. We discuss this research in the context of cognitive psychology since it concerns a general model of hierarchical learning as opposed to a purely stimulus-response model. Gagné found that abstract principles and complex problem-solving skills are acquired with greater facility when more simple and concrete antecedents are learned first. He proposes that complex learning should be preceded by an introduction to subordinate and less complex learning. Thus specific examples of concepts and principles should precede learning of intermediate level abstractions which in turn should precede learning of the most abstract ideas. Similarly, complex problem-solving skills should be taught by introducing the most elementary and necessary components of the skill followed first by higher complex or more inclusive steps in problem-solving, and concluding with the most complex integration of all of the preceding less-inclusive steps. At first sight, there may appear to be a contradiction between Gagné's prescription of serial organization in learning and that proposed by Ausubel. Ausubel recommends presenting the most inclusive and general concepts in a lesson followed by specific facts. Gagné prescribes an orderly sequence beginning with concrete exemplars and the most elementary skills before proceeding to more general and complex learning. The apparent contradiction dissolves when one clearly distinguishes the purpose of each model. Ausubel is concerned with reception learning and ways of maximizing the meaningfulness and stability of learned specifics. Gagné is concerned with ways of optimizing initial learning of abstractions and complex problem-solving skills. The two models explain quite different cognitive processes.

The teacher who intends to employ these models needs to carefully determine the purposes of instruction and then select the model which is most appropriate. If the purpose of the lesson is to introduce the student to many specific facts, then Ausubel's model of subsumption and application of advance organizers is an appropriate choice. The lesson can begin by calling up previously learned concepts and principles and increasing their generality and comprehensiveness by relating them to appropriate subconcepts essential as subsumers for the specifics to follow. On the other hand, if the purpose of the lesson is to introduce the students to a set of principles or problem-solving skills, then Gagné's model of a specifics-to-generalities hierarchy is more appropriate. The lesson should be initiated with familiar and elementary concepts and proceed by elaboration and accretion toward more complex and general exemplars. Figure 10 illustrates a skill hierarchy published by Okey and Gagné (1970). The hierarchy should be read from bottom to top. Subordinate skills are subsumed within higher order skills culminating at the top in the most general skill. A connection between a subordinate skill and its nearest superordinate skill is shown by a solid line in the hierarchy.

When planning a skill hierarchy, one must first identify the skill to be learned. Then, the next nearest subordinate step must be identified and the necessary skills for its completion determined. Each of these skills in turn is analyzed to determine the nearest subordinate skill required for its completion. By this analysis, the hierarchy is eventually broken down until the most elementary tasks have been identified. Curriculum materials are organized using the hierarchy as a lesson plan, the most elementary skills being presented first, followed by the superordinate skills. The curriculum is organized so that each lower order skill precedes and leads into the next higher order skill. If the student fails to master the ultimate skill, then he is tested for each subordinate skill to determine which one has not been acquired. The pupil is given remedial training in subordinate skills and allowed once again to attempt the ultimate skill. By this method of differential analysis of subordinate skill attainment, essential to ultimate skill mastery, a highly efficient learning hierarchy can be created. Gagné has developed a systematic quantitative method of analyzing pupil performance to determine what subordinate learning is necessary for satisfactory completion of higher order tasks. His publication should be consulted for details (Gagné 1967).

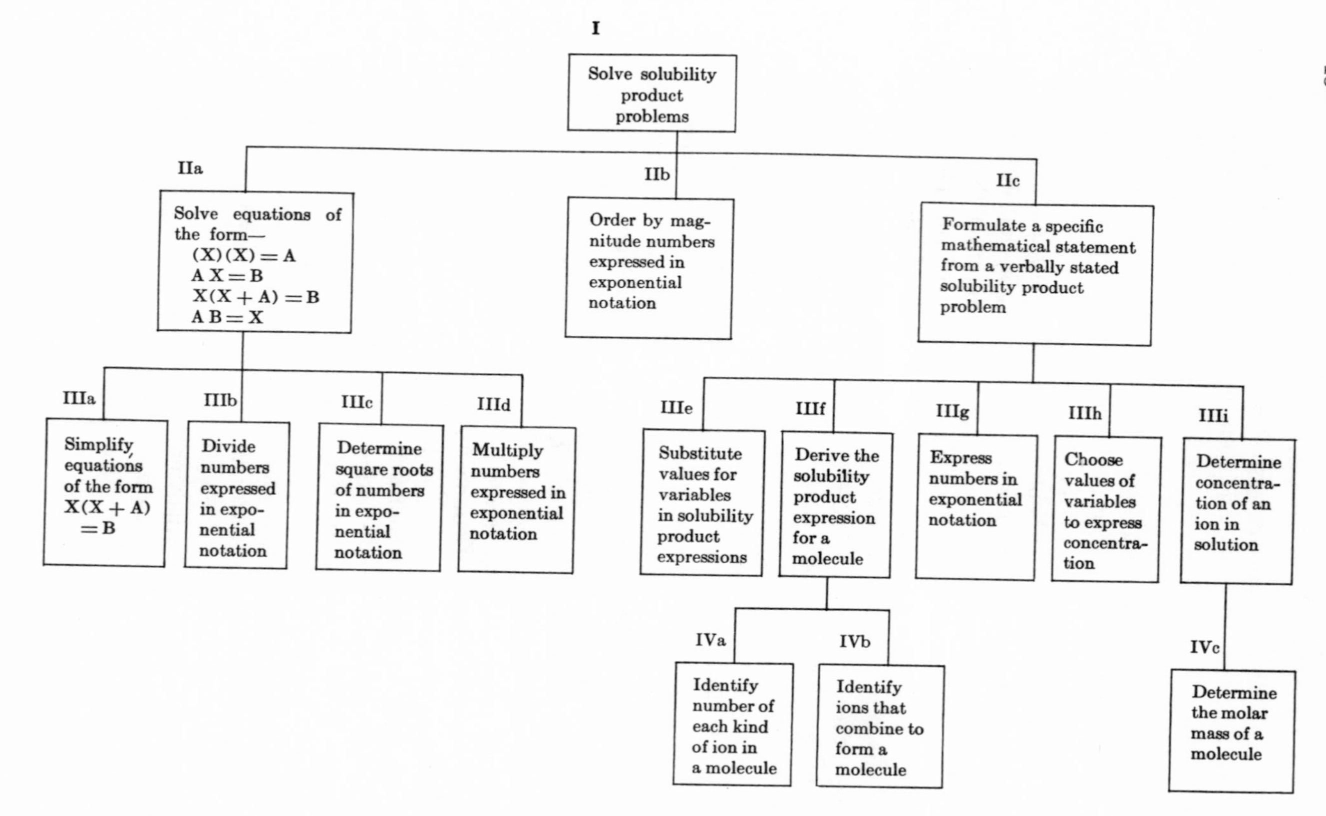

Figure 10 A Skill Hierarchy Published by Okey and Gagné

Ausubel and Gagné propose hierarchical models of learning. They differ in the kind of learning they attempt to explain and the sequential direction in which ideas should be organized to achieve their respective learning objectives. Gagné's model of learning and his empirical method of hierarchical analysis of principle and skill learning are valuable aids to the teacher in planning lessons to teach generalizations and problem-solving.

We conclude our discussion of cognitive learning models by summarizing some of J. S. Bruner's writings on concept attainment and structure in teaching. Bruner proposes that economy in thinking and responding requires that we categorize phenomena according to the attributes they hold in common. An attribute is a property or characteristic of an object which allows us to recognize it as an entity. Thus, most perceptual cues can be used as attributes provided we are aware of their association with an object. Color, texture, form, size, number of parts, position, and sound are examples of attributes. We categorize certain animals having four legs, a tail, and a barking voice as dogs. We have thus created a concept of dog based on the number of legs, presence or absence of tail and a barking voice as attributes. We also generate more abstract concepts such as enemy or friend, peer or superior, artisan or professional. Categories of these kinds help us respond parsimoniously to phenomena. By assigning newly encountered phenomena to previously formed categories, we can cope with the new instances in predetermined ways without making a detailed analysis of each one. We therefore categorize a stranger as friendly, aggressive, timid, or uninterested and make appropriate social responses. Categorization requires that the attributes used to separate phenomena have variation in value. Thus, if all objects in our environment were the same color, we could not use this quality as a categorizing property. We attend to variations in attribute value when forming concepts. We must identify the attributes of the concept and specify the values of the attributes which taken together characterize the concept. When we identify photosynthetic plants as living things containing cells surrounded by a wall and possessing chloropryll, we implicitly recognize that the attributes of this category can assume other values. There are non-living things, things without cells, cells with little or no wall material, and some things contain no chlorophyll. For purposes of this discussion, we define a concept as a category, set apart from other categories of things, based on the attribute values assigned to the objects in the category. Each concept is characterized by the set of attribute values assigned to it. A concept is set apart from a similar concept by the unique attribute values assigned to it. Cows and dogs both are animals with four legs and a tail, but cows have horns and dogs do not. When teaching science concepts, the teacher does well to carefully identify the defining attributes of the concept. These should be presented as positive instances of the things representing the concept. Negative instances (those not falling within the category) should be cited to clearly differentiate the concept from its near relatives.

Bruner has studied the strategies people use in acquiring concepts (Bruner et al. 1956). He was interested in finding the methods people use to identify a concept when they are presented with a large array of objects, some representing instances of the concept and others not. The subjects were presented with an array of cards containing patterns of various shapes and colors. Some of the cards contained borders, others did not. All of the cards contained center figures varying in shape (square, circle, or cross), in color (red, green, or black), and in number (single, double, or triple). Each card thus combines four attributes: figure shape, figure number, figure color, and presence or absence of borders. Each attribute has three values as listed above. Each subject was told that the experimenter had a concept in mind and that the subject was to identify the concept. For example, the experimenter might choose as a concept red circles or, two borders and green figures. The subject was not told, of course, what concept the experimenter had in mind. The subject's task was to attain the concept by testing cards shown in Figure 11 for instances of the concept. The procedure was for the subject to select a card, and then to be told by the experimenter whether or not the card was an instance of the concept. With these data in mind, the subject would select another card in an attempt to determine further which attributes were necessary.

For example, suppose the experimenter had in mind the

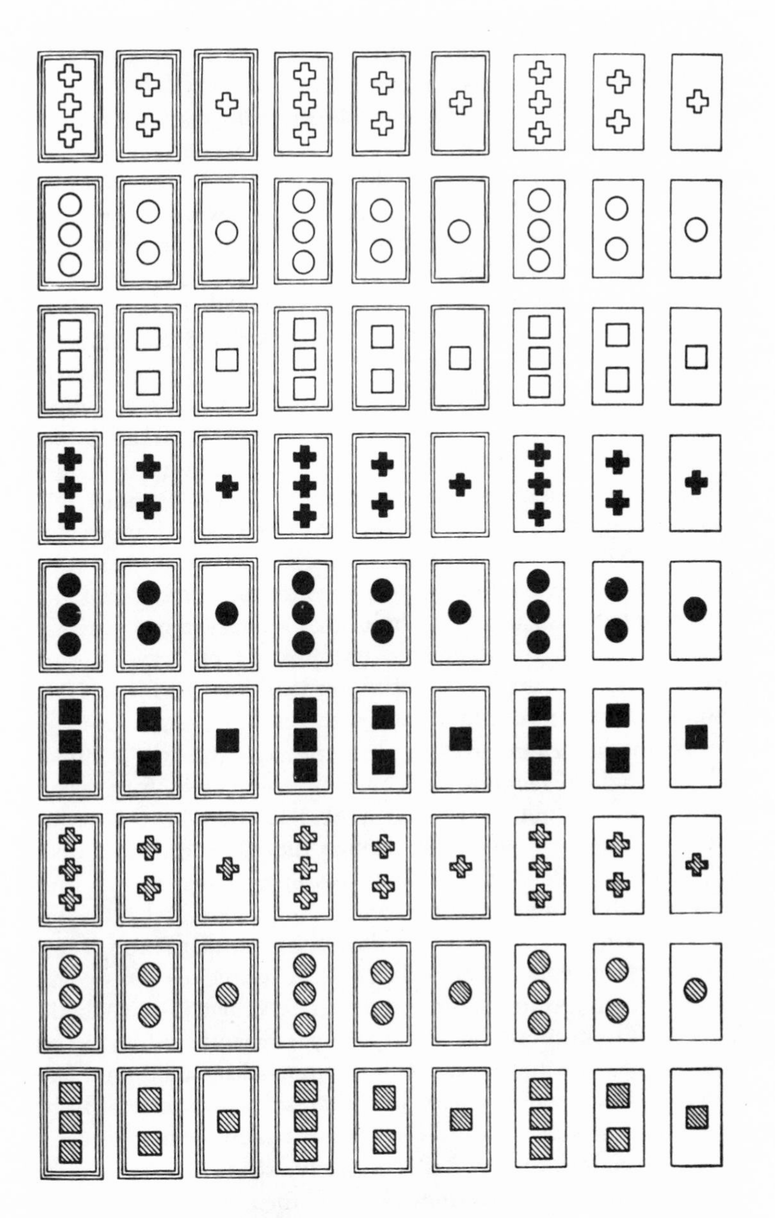

Figure 11 Bruner's Cards

concept of red circles and the subject chose a card on the first try with three red circles and two borders. The experimenter would affirm the card as a correct instance. Now the subject must determine what it is about the card that made it a correct instance. It might be the borders, the number of figures, their color, or their shape. The subject would continue selecting cards and inferring from the experimenter's responses which attributes were significant. When the subject felt he had eliminated the extraneous attributes and found the proper combination, he announced his conclusion and was told whether he was correct. The reader may feel that identifying cards and the strategies people use to identify categories of them is a bit far removed from teaching science. Before going further, we briefly demonstrate the relevance of this general problem to modern practices of science teaching. The use of discovery and enquiry techniques in teaching provide the pupil with subject matter tasks quite similar to the card tasks used in Bruner's study. Suppose, for example, that we want the pupil to invent his own classification scheme for a restricted group of plants or animals by examining its morphology. Clearly, the pupil must identify those attributes which allow him to reasonably group a set of organisms. He must develop a strategy to identify the attributes held in common by several members of the whole array.

As another example, we could provide the naive student with longitudinal sections of stem, root, stolon, branch, and floral apices, and ask him to develop a plan to describe the various regions of development by examining the tissue organization in each section. This task clearly requires categorizing skills. Strategies the student might employ to accomplish this task could be similar to those employed by Bruner's subjects in identifying concepts by selecting cards. A strategy is a systematic way of selecting combinations of attribute values to test whether they are instances of the concept. An efficient strategy is one which yields the most information from each trial, minimizes cognitive strain, and produces an early correct conclusion. Bruner identified four strategies used in concept attainment: (1) simultaneous-scanning strategy, (2) successive-scanning strategy, (3) conservative-focussing strategy, and (4) focus-gambling strategy.

We limit our discussion to strategies appropriate to the identification of conjunctive concepts. (A conjunctive concept is defined by the presence of the appropriate value of several attributes. For example, the presence of three figures, redness, and circles on a card, thus, three red circles, is a case of a conjunctive concept.)

Simultaneous Scanning

Given the cards shown in Figure 11, there are 255 possible ways of grouping instances (combinations of figure, number, color, and border) into conjunctive concepts. When the subject selects a card which is a positive instance, he gathers information in the pattern on the card which allows him to deduce that 240 of these combinations are no longer relevant. Similarly, a proper selection of the next card allows him to eliminate other combinations of characteristics. Eventually, if the subject can keep in mind all of the combinations that have been eliminated, he identifies the only remaining possible combination and hence solves the problem. In simultaneous-scanning strategy, the subject uses each positive instance (each correctly identified card) to deduce which combinations of attribute values are no longer valid. This is a very demanding strategy since the subject must remember which combinations of card characteristics have been previously rejected in order to narrow the range of subsequent alternatives. Basically this is a process of identification by elimination of all possible invalid combinations as deduced from the correct instances previously chosen. The technique is not very efficient since it places a great deal of strain on the subject's memory, and usually fails since the subject cannot remember which characteristics have been eliminated. The strategy is called simultaneous scanning since the subject must keep in mind simultaneously all of the rejected hypotheses in order to narrow his range of choices to the final remaining correct combination of attributes.

Successive Scanning

This stategy is less demanding than the simultaneous-scanning strategy. Instead of keeping several hypotheses in mind simultaneously, the subject chooses one hypothesis such as *red is the feature common to all correct cards,* and chooses instances containing red to test the hypothesis. The subject attempts to make a global estimate of each correct characteristic of the concept and by successively testing each one he hopes to hit upon the right combination of characteristics. This is called successive-scanning strategy since the subject tests individual hypotheses about the correct characteristic one at a time in succession. The technique is inefficient since the subject may select redundant cards which give no new information, cards which were used in testing other hypotheses.

Conservative Focussing

In this strategy, each attribute is tested by selecting a card that is different from a focus card in only one attribute. If the new card is still a positive instance, then the subject knows that the varied attribute is not part of the concept. If, however, the changed attribute yields a negative instance, then the subject knows that attribute to be part of the concept. By careful testing of each attribute value, the subject eventually specifies the necessary combination of attributes to produce the concept. Suppose, for example, the concept to be attained is "red circles." Assume the subject encounters a positive card with three red circles and two borders. This card becomes the focus card and each variable is examined by selecting additional cards. The selection sequence is given below. A plus sign in parenthesis means the card is a positive instance of the concept, a minus sign in parentheses that the card is a negative instance.

Focus card: 3 red circles, 2 borders (+)

2 red circles, 2 borders (+)	First decision: eliminate "three figures" as a relevant variable
3 green circles, 2 borders (−)	Second decision: retain red as relevant attribute value
3 red crosses, 2 borders (−)	Third decision: retain circle as relevant attribute value

3 red circles, 1 border (+)	Fourth decision: eliminate "two borders" as relevant attribute value

Conclusion: the concept is "red circles."

This technique differs from successive-scanning strategy in that the subject focusses on a correct instance and systematically tests each attribute value to determine which ones are relevant. In successive-scanning strategy, you recall, the subject hypothesizes that an attribute value is one common to all correct instances and tests his hypothesis by selecting appropriate cards. The conservative-focussing strategy is more efficient since the subject uses a *correct instance* as a point of reference and selects additional cards to test each attribute value individually.

Focus Gambling

In this stategy the subject focusses on a correct card, but varies more than one attribute at a time. In other words, instead of testing each characteristic by selecting cards which differ by only one characteristic at a time, the subject selects cards which differ by two or more characteristics each time. This strategy can yield early success if cards are chosen which yield a positive example each time. If, however, the subject makes a bad choice (finds a negative card), he cannot tell which attribute was essential and therefore must revert to the less efficient method of simultaneous-scanning to test hypotheses. This stategy is called gambling since the subject takes a chance in varying two attributes at once. If the subject encounters a negative instance (a card not satisfying the conditions of the concept) he can easily be confused and must revert to a less efficient strategy. We have more to say about these strategies when we apply them to practical problems of teaching concepts and facilitating pupil problem solving.

Bruner has given some attention to practical problems of curriculum organization. In his insightful article on cognitive growth (1964), he identifies three stages of human cognitive development; (1) enactive, (2) iconic, and (3) symbolic. Enactive representations of the world are the first to be acquired. These include manipulative skills and motor activities which represent ways of acting upon the environment. At a later point in cognitive growth, iconic or spatial representations of the world are acquired. At this stage, percepts are organized in patterned spatial arrays and imagery is the ascendent organizing scheme used to represent experience. Ultimately, symbolic patterns such as language and numerical symbols are acquired. Symbolic representations of experience are of course the most sophisticated of the three kinds cited and allow considerable flexibility in representing prior experience and to predict and explain future experiences.

Bruner suggests that curriculum sequences can be organized in stages which parallel the stages of cognitive growth (1967). Topics in the discipline to be taught can be presented in a sequence containing, (1) the ways of manipulating the environment, (2) the spatial imagery used in the discipline, and (3) the symbolic inventions in the substantive field. Bruner concedes that mature students who have developed a facility with language may not need to progress through each of the three steps. Their language skills can be used to represent the fundamental characteristics of the discipline. However, there is a clear danger that if the students have not had sufficient prior enactive and iconic introductions to a substantive area, the symbolic presentation may exceed their cognitive capacity. One task of the teacher is to assess the pupil's prior learning and determine the level of presentation for introducing the material.

Bruner has also considered the question of what constitutes structure in a discipline (1962). He proposes that the structure of a discipline is the set of principles in a field which allows one to determine how things are related. To teach the structure of a discipline is to present the over-arching principles that integrate specific instances and allow the pupil to classify new instances as elements subsumed within a principle. In brief, he states, to learn the structure of a discipline is to learn how things are related. A lesson can be organized by using the general principles of a field as integrating themes to which specific examples are related as the lesson sequence unfolds. The critical task for the teacher is to identify the major principles of a field that can be used as themes. These principles should be sufficiently inclusive to allow their application to a broad range of related phenomena. They should be sufficiently differentiated to allow the pupil to know when a principle is applicable as an explanation of phenomena and when it is inappropriate. By this procedure, transfer of training is optimal and the pupil gains maximum use of the principle in organizing and categorizing new relevant instances. Examples of some biological principles suitable for use as structural themes in teaching are adaptation, energy flow, continuity of genetic inheritance, life cycles, feedback control of biological processes, and irritability in living systems.

The models of learning proposed by Ausubel, Bruner, and Gagné share a common property; they are concerned with the role of proactive facilitation in learning. Proactive facilitation is a psychological principle. It can be stated in general terms as follows: Prior learning in a sequence, when properly organized and selected for its level of generality or abstractness, can facilitate subsequent learning. Ausubel focuses on the problem of specific learning and proposes that advance organizing of conceptual information will facilitate learning of subsequent related specifics. Gagné conceptualizes learning as a hierarchical process and suggests that principle and problem-solving learning can be facilitated when the student is introduced to subordinate (less complex) learning tasks prior to more complex tasks. Bruner in a similar view recommends a sequential build up of experience proceeding through enactive, iconic, and symbolic presentations. The enactive and iconic experiences proactively facilitate symbolic learning. Bruner's concept of structure in teaching, defined as the use of general principles which facilitate subsequent learning of related specifics, clearly falls within the category of proactive facilitation. Each theorist provides unique ways of employing the proactive facilitation principle depending on the objective of the lesson. We illustrate the use of these various schemes in organizing lessons in Chapter Three.

A Biopsychological Theory of Learning and Communication

This theory is built on concepts of biological evolution and psychological chaining. It is most useful in explaining the sequential organization of communication particularly with reference to the flow of ideas during verbal communication. The flow of ideas, their relatedness to one another in a sequence, and their recurrence throughout a communication is related to knowledge acquisition. We examine those factors in human evolution and cognitive maturation that influence communication organization and its reception. The theoretical principles discussed are, (1) the biological origin of verbal communication patterns and their effect on verbal learning; (2) the psychological principles of verbal learning derived from the theory; and (3) some methods of communication structure analysis. (Fuller accounts of both principles and methods are found in Anderson 1969 and 1971).

The theory assumes that human verbal communication is a serial phenomenon. Ideas are communicated in a series of individual statements called discourse units. A discourse unit is the equivalent of a clause in written discourse. The structure of a communication sequence is the continuity of ideas from one discourse unit to the next. Given a stream of discourse units, the amount of structure in the communication is the degree of idea linkage between consecutive statements. Structure also includes the recurrence of the same idea throughout the sequence of discourse units. The amount of structure in such a sequence is directly related to the number of verbal elements shared by contiguous discourse units. The presence of shared elements in contiguous discourse units is called *commonality*. Commonality of verbal elements in contiguous discourse units is illustrated in the model displayed as Figure 12.

Four discourse units are represented as rectangles. Each discourse unit contains words representing ideas. These, of course, are verbal elements and are symbolized in the figure by alphabet letters. Commonality is the repetition of one or more ideas in consecutive discourse units. The recurrence of the same verbal element in several discourse units serves as an extended connec-

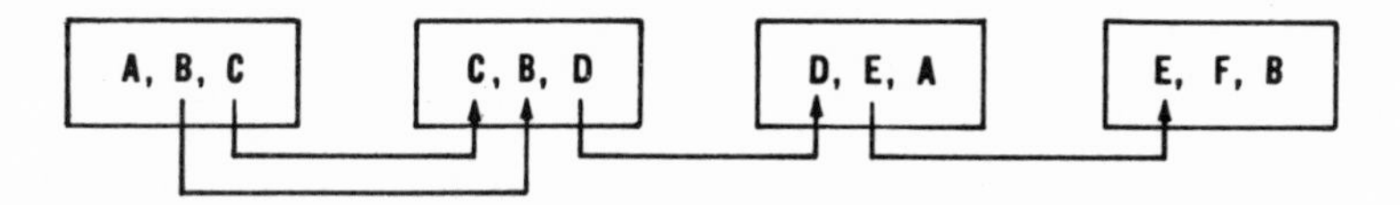

Figure 12 Commonality
Discourse units, shown as rectangles, contain verbal elements, shown by arrows linking the common elements in consecutive pairs of discourse units.

tion among the several units as does element A in Figure 12. This connection of ideas between consecutive statements and the recurrence of ideas at longer intervals is an obvious feature of meaningful communication. Basically it is a periodic phenomenon since connections between consecutive statements can occur only if an idea is repeated in the next statement. Likewise, appearances of the same idea again and again in a communication sequence is a periodic or at least a repetitive event. When we speak of commonality in communication then, we are talking about the periodic appearance of the same verbal element in consecutive discourse units thereby giving them connectedness.

In addition to commonality, an equally obvious characterisic of communication is the fact that efficient communication must continuously include some new ideas. Repetition of ideas is not sufficient to build up quantities of new knowledge and hence the need to continuously introduce new thoughts. The accretion of new thoughts in a communication sequence is called *progression*. Whereas commonality is the repetition of verbal elements linking discource units together, progression is the rate at which new verbal elements appear in the communication sequence. A carefully prepared communication should provide the proper mix of commonality and progression to maintain continuity of ideas and to introduce a sufficient number of new ideas to sustain pupil interest and allow accretion of new thoughts.

We will explore and biological origins of commonality and progression in communication and explain the psychological necessity for the proper blend of these qualities to maximize human reception of the communication. The underlying assumptions of the biopsychological theory are:

1. The natural environment favored the evolution of organisms possessing stimulus receptors and nervous systems sensitive to periodic stimuli.
2. During human ontogeny, visual scanning of the environment produces a succession of images on the retina of the eye wherein each image contains some figural elements in common with contiguous images. These experiences predispose the organism to anticipate that successive stimuli will have properties in common.
3. Language and thought are products of these genetic influences. They are both in part serial processes wherein contiguous units hold elements in common.
4. Acquisition of verbal material is enhanced when contiguous verbal statements (stimuli) in a communication contain identical verbal elements in addition to new verbal elements.

According to Darwinian evolution theory, the form and function of extant living organisms can be explained as the product of successive changes in offsping through many generations. The changes are produced by natural selection—a process by which environmental factors favor the survival of those organisms capable of using the environment for their own benefit. Thus, those organisms best adapted to the environment survive and produce offspring whose form and function are perhaps better adapted to the environment than those of the parents. Through many generations of this selection process, organisms evolve in complexity and in capacity to exploit the environment. We may ask then what environmental factors may have contributed to the development of periodicity in communication patterns of higher animals.

There are many periodic phenomena in the environment which surely must have been present very early in the evolution of living things. Among these are cycles of light and darkness, and periodic motions of water masses such as waves and tides. Those organisms capable of using the periodic phenomena for survival would succeed in the environment and give rise to offspring better adapted to use these affects. Chart 1 lists the environmental periodic influences which may have favored the

CHART 1 PERIODICITY

Stage	*Environmental Factor*	*Adaptive Response*
Molecule	Light waves: periodic electromagnetic radiation	Incorporation of light-absorbing compounds in infracellular aggregates enhancing energy reception
Cell	Same as above, and also diurnal light cycles	Simple photosensitive cellular organelles enhanced photoaxis and allowed organism to locomote to thriving primary food producers
Multicell	Periodic motion of water masses: tides and surface waves	Organisms with simple reflexive nerve system favored by greater autonomy and resistance to random effects of water motion
Advanced Metazoa	Light and dark cycles; space-filling light rays emanating from illuminated objects	Integration of photosensory stimulation with locomotion through mediation of complex nervous system: efficient response to dangers and sources of food

survival of increasingly complex organisms sensitive to periodic stimuli at each level of evolution.

The presence of periodic light radiation may have favored the development of complex photoreceptors as summarized in Chart 2. The appearance of complex light focussing eyes in advanced animals allowed them to perceive the visual environment with great detail. When the eye scans the horizon, it produces a succession of retinal images with overlapping figural content. Given, in addition, a complex nervous system maximally sensitive to repetitive stimulation, it is proposed that the organism (such as man) developed a perceptual bias to anticipate and maximally respond to stimuli containing periodic properties. Moreover, early man could have developed language sequences which complemented this bias; namely, to vocalize sequences with periodic utterances and in such a pattern that the flow was similar to the visual patterns produced while scanning the

CHART 2 DISTRIBUTION OF VISUAL PIGMENTS IN LIVING PHOTOSENSITIVE ORGANISMS AND THEIR PHOTORECEPTORS

Organism	*Pigment* *	*Receptor*
Protozoa	C	Stigmata
Coelenterates		Unicellular eyespots and ocelli
Flatworms		Same
Annelids	R	Unicellular eyespots, compound eyespots, and ocelli or camera-style eyes
Molluscs	R_1	Compound eyespots and ocelli or camera-style eyes
Arthropods	R_1	Ocelli or compound eyes (ommatidia)
Fish and Reptiles	R_1, R_2	Lens-containing eyes
Mammals	R_1	Lens-containing eyes with binocular vision

* C—beta-carotene, R—retinene, R_1—retinene one, R_2—retinene two

horizon. Thus we see two major factors contributed to the development of language commonality: (1) the organic functions of a nervous system and stimulus receptors maximally adapted to receive periodic stimulation, and (2) visual experiences characterized by successive reception of overlapping images. These two factors, taken together, make highly probable that a complex organism like man would develop a sequential language with overlapping distributions of words in successive utterances.

We may conclude, therefore, that some commonality in communication sequences is desirable to assure optimal receptivity to and cognitive encoding of the information. Too much repetition is deleterious since the nervous system rapidly adapts to excessively repetitious material and fails to respond. Therefore, to ensure effective reception of a communication there should be some commonality to satisfy the perceptual bias for repetition and continuity in reception, and also some progression to maintain arousal and peaked sensitivity to the information flow.

There are several ways of organizing content to secure commonality among successive discourse units in a communication. Each organizational mode is called a dimension. There are three dimensions: (1) spatial, (2) chronological, and (3) derived. A plan or guide in preparing a lesson sequence uses a dimension. A spatial dimension is used when teaching the organization of physical systems such as anatomy, plant and animal community structure, or the structure of an apparatus. The plan consists of identifying a peripheral or a central component and systematically describing each additional component in order of occurrence in the object itself. In this way, spatial continuity is maintained and each statement in the sequence flows logically into the next since each contiguous pair of statements contains references to common spatial characteristics. For example in teaching circulatory system anatomy, one may use a spatial dimension by starting with (1) a description of the heart, continuing with (2) pulmonary vessels, and concluding with (3) general systemic vessels. This is, no doubt, the most primitive organizational dimension one can use. A chronological dimension lists the events occurring in a process in such an order that the most related events are listed together. Thus in a chemical pathway consisting of several intermediate reactions, the reactions should be taught in the order that they occur naturally so that products of one step become the reactants of the next step, thereby conferring commonality on the sequence of ideas.

Finally, derived dimensions are the most abstract plans for organizing content. These include any sequential arrangement of ideas which, by the use of themes running throughout, or the use of linking ideas between successive statements, or of logical patterns of hierarchical organization, produce symbolic commonality among discourse units in the communication. Thus, language and the ideas it represents are used to create overlapping distribution of content in consecutive discourse units in a communication. The various patterns that can be used are discussed in the section on serial learning. Their main function is to produce a pattern simulated by the model shown in Figure 12 or an elaboration thereof.

Relationships exist between the concept of commonality in communication and the psychological principle of response chaining. Response chaining should be directly related to the amount of commonality in a communication sequence. When commonality is optimal, and there is continuity of ideas from one statement to the next in a communication, then the series of responses aroused by the communication will also have continuity of elements from one to the next. That is, as the student hears the communication sequence, he represents it cognitively as a series of verbal responses approximately equivalent to the series of communicated statements. If the statements have commonality, then the responses aroused by them and closely approximating their organization also have commonality. Each response in the series has some verbal elements in common with the next response aroused. Under these conditions, we expect the responses to be linked together in a chain. Two necessary conditions for chaining are satisfied. (1) Each response in sequence serves as a discriminative stimulus for the next response since it has some verbal elements in common with the succeeding response. Given the student's perceptual bias to anticipate continuity of flow of ideas, the next response is anticipated by its nearest preceding response when commonality is high and the preceding response has high stimulus value for the succeeding response; and (2) The succeeding response aroused at each step in the sequence serves as a reinforcer for the preceding response when commonality is high since it satisfies the student's anticipatory bias. Also, the very repetition of the continuous ideas partially reinforces the preceding response. The psychological value of commonality in producing stable, orderly sequences of responses rests in the high probability of response chain formation. When, however, commonality is low, chaining is depressed and the knowledge so acquired is less orderly and not as stable.

Some methods of assessing commonality and progression in verbal communications are described. These methods are used to analyze two sample lessons presented in Chapter Three. The fundamental concepts presented here must be understood before the analyses can become meaningful. A written communication or a transcription of a tape recorded lesson is broken into individual discourse units. A discourse unit is a complete grammatical clause (a statement having a subject and a predicate).

(Special rules have been developed to handle various cases; Anderson 1971.) Each discourse unit is examined for all the substantive words it contains. Each substantive word is assigned a code number. This code number is used thereafter to represent the word when it appears in subsequent discourse units. Each coded word represents a verbal element. Now, to prepare the communication for quantitative analysis of commonality and progression, each discourse unit is labeled with the code numbers it contains. An example is given here.

1. All right, we'll go on now to talk about red blood cells ^{1}, the second part of the blood ^{2}, what they do. 1,2
2. We mentioned hemoglobin ^{3} red blood cells ^{1} being to a large extent made up of this protein ^{4}. 3,1,4
3. This material ^{3} enables the red blood cells ^{1} to pick up oxygen ^{5} 3,1,5
4. So the second function ^{6}, we can say, is that cells ^{7} carry oxygen ^{5}. 6,7,5

Four discourse units are given. The code number assigned to each verbal element in a discourse unit is shown as a superscript. Note that whenever the verbal element is repeated in a subsequent discourse unit the same code number is assigned. The verbal elements in each discourse unit are represented at the right by their assigned code numbers. Thus we gain a short-hand notation of the key substantive terms in each discourse unit. These code numbers are assigned to all discourse units in the total communication.

There are two basic coefficients used to assess commonality. They are the fundamental coefficient (B_1) and the weighted coefficient (B_2). Each coefficient is computed for a pair of discourse units and all consecutive pairs of discourse units in a communication are analyzed. The fundamental coefficient is the ratio of the total number of matched verbal elements in a pair of discourse units divided by the total number of elements within the pair. The formula for the fundamental coefficient is:

$$B_1 = \frac{n_1}{n_0 + n_1}$$

where n_1 is the total number of matched elements in a pair of discourse units and n_0 is the number of unmatched elements. To apply the coefficient one simply counts the number of repeated code numbers in a pair of discourse units and substitutes this for n_1, and counts the number of non-repeated code numbers in a pair to find n_0. The B_1 is obtained for each pair of discourse units in succession; thus, for units 1 and 2, 2 and 3, 3 and 4, and so forth. For example, of the first pair of discourse units (units 1 and 2) shown above, each contains the element number 1. Therefore, since numbers 1 occurs two times in the pair, $n_1=2$. All totalled, there are three unmatched elements, namely, 2, 3, and 4. Therefore, the $B_1=2/\ 3+2=0.40$. In like manner we compute a B_1 value for units 2 and 3. It is $B_1=4/\ 2+4=0.67$. The B_1 coefficient is obviously a direct measure of the amount of commonality in successive pairs of discourse units. At the conclusion of computing the B_1 values for all consecutive pairs of units, the mean value is obtained (B_1) which is simply the sum of all B_1 values in the list divided by their number. B_1 gives an estimate of the average commonality for a whole communication.

The weighted coefficient (B_2) is a modified fundamental coefficient. It is defined as

$$B_2=1-\left[\frac{n_0}{n_0+n_1}\cdot\left(\frac{F'+F''}{\Sigma f}\right)^{\frac{1}{2}}\right]$$

where n_0 and n_1 are the same as in B_1. The B_2 coefficient assesses the amount of commonality in a pair of discourse units in relation to the potency of the unmatched elements (n_0) in the unit pair. The term potency refers here to the frequency of occurrence of the elements in the whole communication. To compute B_2 values (these are usually calculated by computer) one must know the frequency of occurrence of an element in the whole communication. The total number of times each element occurs in a lesson is tabulated. In the B_2 formula F' and F'' are frequency values. To compute the formula, one examines the *unmatched* elements in the first discourse unit. He then examines the total frequency of occurrence of each unmatched element in the whole lesson. That frequency which is *larger* (the larger number) is substituted for F'. Then, the unmatched elements in the second discourse unit of the pair are determined and the frequency of occurrence which is greatest is substituted for F″. If, of course, there is only one unmatched element in either unit, then only its total frequency can be used as a value for the appropriate F term. The denominator Σf is simply the total frequency of all elements in the communication. We will use the same discourse units in computing B_2 values. In discourse units 1 and 2, the first discourse unit has one unmatched element, number 2. Suppose in the whole lesson it occurs 10 times. Since it is the only unmatched element we have to use its frequency for F′; namely $F' = 10$. In discourse unit 2, elements 3 and 4 are unmatched. Assume in the whole lesson element 3 occurs 6 times and 4 occurs 4 times. We choose the larger value for F″, namely, 6. For this lesson assume $\Sigma f = 400$. (Σf is a constant for the lesson when computing B_2 values.) Therefore, the B_2 value for the first pair of discourse units is:

$$B_2 = 1 - \left[\frac{3}{3+2} \cdot \left(\frac{10+6}{400} \right)^{\frac{1}{2}} \right]$$

The exponent to the ½ power tells us to take the square root of the parenthetical expression; thus, $B_2 = 1 - (0.6 \cdot 0.2) = 0.88$. A B_2 value is obtained for each consecutive pair of discourse units and a mean value is computed for the whole lesson.

The main purpose of the B_2 coefficient is to plot a graph called a Kinetogram. The abscissa (horizontal axis) of the graph is marked off in discourse units and the ordinate is divided into B_2 units. We can thereby plot variation in B_2 values as a function of time (successive discourse units). A Kinetogram segment is shown in Figure 13. The B_2 value for each pair of discourse units has been plotted and connected by lines. The abscissa is placed at the top of the graph to give us a reference line to determine how closely the plotted lines approach $B_2 = 1.0$. When the line on the graph tends upward or fluctuates close to the abscissa, commonality is high and there are few high frequency unmatched elements in the pairs of discourse units. When, however, the graph line declines or fluctuates at a depressed level, then commonality is lower and high frequency elements are not being matched in consecutive statements. The Kinetogram is useful as

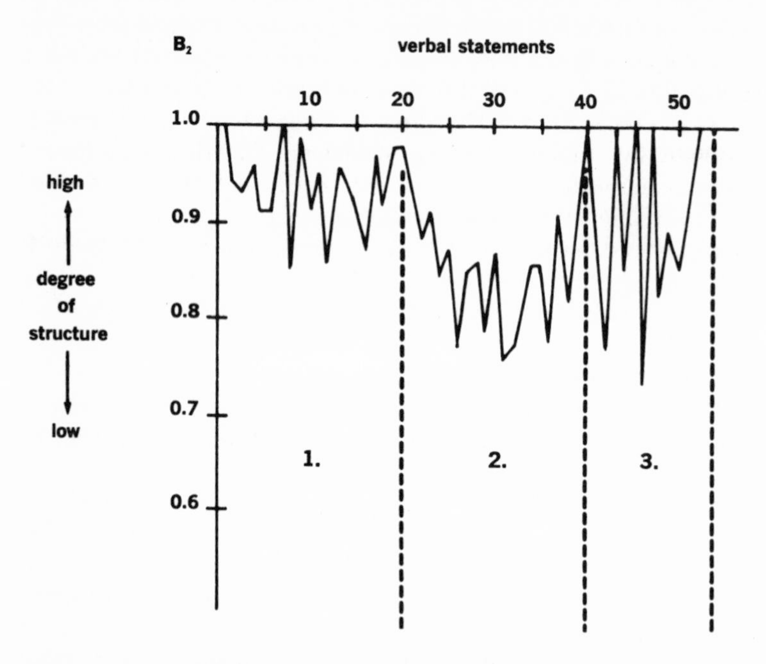

Figure 13 Sample Kinetogram
Three variations of degree of structure are shown. In section 1, structure is high: the graph line fluctuates near the abscissa. In section 2 the series of verbal statements is lower in structure: the trace is clearly more depressed here. Section 3 illustrates a segment of discourse in which ideas are presented in bursts or quantized units: the downward-directed spikes anchored on the abscissa are signs supporting this.

a visual display of the continuity of flow of ideas in a lesson. When the graph line is elevated, the flow is continuous or only mildly discontinuous. When the graph line is depressed, the flow of ideas is highly discontinuous. When the graph contains several downward directed spikes with final points anchored on the abscissa, it means ideas are being presented in short discontinuous bursts. These various signs are explained in the legend of Figure 13.

We will use B_1 coefficients and Kinetograms to analyze some sample lesson segments presented in Chapter Three. A Kinetogram can be used to break the lesson into short internal sequences called spans. Spans are blocks of discourse organized around a single idea or a series of discourse units with high structure—that is, high commonality. The presence of a theme in the span is assessed by a theme activity coefficient. The theme coefficient (technically called a relative activity coefficient, RAC) is defined as the frequency of occurrence of the most active element in a span divided by the number of discourse units in the span. If RAC approaches zero, there is little theme activity—there is no main idea running throughout the span. When RAC approaches a value of 1.0, there is a clearly identified thread of an idea running throughout the span. This coefficient allows us to identify only the existence of explicit themes. Inferred themes, such as implied principles or integrating themes introduced prior to the span, cannot be detected by use of RAC.

The biopsychological theory of learning predicts that knowledge acquisition is directly related to the amount of commonality in a communication. However, problem-solving activity and classroom discussion may be enhanced by appropriate selective reductions in commonality, thereby challenging the pupils to supply (through analysis and interpolation) some of the missing logical steps in that segment of the lesson.

The theory is very useful in thinking about the serial organization of lessons and creating ways of linking ideas to produce the most logical flow. Moreover, the quantitative system of analysis allows a highly objective analysis of how completely the continuity in flow of ideas has been achieved.

Conceptually the theory stands in the middle ground between association and cognitive learning models. It is not molecular as are the theories of stimulus-response psychologists. Nor is it as broad in its scope as the very general theories of some cognitive psychologists. It clearly provides some linkage of ideas between the vast strata of association theories and cognitive models. In relation to communication models, it also is a middle ground system. It is not concerned with the structure of individual statements at the molecular level nor is it applicable to understanding the more abstract qualities of connotation in language. Rather, it concerns the intermediate level of the flow of ideas among statements in a communication. Therein lies a limitation of the model. It is restricted to an explanation of the effects of continuity and periodicity in communication on knowledge and skill acquisition. To the extent of this limitation, other theories must be called upon to explain the more global issues of affect, origins of creative behavior, and methods of concept learning. We now turn our discussion to a synthesis of these various models as we discuss three kinds of organization in planning lessons, namely, (1) serial learning, (2) cluster learning, and (3) problem solving.

Serial Learning

In Chapter One, we briefly discussed two ways of organizing content for teaching knowledge. These were serial-centered and cluster-centered organizations. We now expand this discussion in view of the general learning principles given at the beginning of this chapter. Serial learning is considered first. Some content is best organized in a serial way, with a linear sequence of thoughts. Each thought is fully developed independent of all others. There is little attempt to interrelate thoughts through multiple comparisons. A flow chart of a serial lesson in comparison to a cluster-type lesson is shown in Chart 3. The topic of the lesson is cell membrane structure. The examples cited in Chart 3 are simple illustrations of the differences of flow in serial-centered and cluster-centered lesson outlines.

Lessons using a serial-centered plan should take advantage of content to maximize linkage of ideas in moving from one thought to the next. Theoretically, well organized serial-centered lessons arouse cognitive response chains, thus accounting for student acquisition of the linear-sequenced material. When the communication flow maximizes continuity of ideas from one statement to the next and the statements are organized in small steps, chaining should be facilitated. The following are devices for achieving highly organized serial lessons: 1) cascaded chains, (2) principles and concepts as themes, (3) models as themes, (4) hierarchies, and 5) application of the eight cell coordinate model presented in Chapter One.

Chart 3 Lesson Flow

Serial Lesson	*Cluster Lesson*
Molecular components of cell membrane: lipids, proteins, and carbohydrates	Molecular components of cell membrane: comparative structure of lipids, proteins, and carbohydrates
Bilayer model of Danielli and Davson	Bilayer model of Danielli and Davson
Robertson model of unit membrane —description of lipid and protein organization	Robertson model of unit membrane in relation to the Danielli-Davson model
Mosaic membrane models: lipid and protein organization	Mosaic membrane models: structural features compared to Danielli-Davson and Robertson models; the role of lipids and proteins in each

Cascaded Chains

Content composed of highly complex and lengthy descriptions may be difficult to assimilate if it is presented in a simple linear fashion. Thus even though each individual thought in the lesson has high commonality with its preceding thought, the mass of information communicated may exceed what the student can efficiently encode and categorize into meaningful blocks of information. One way of overcoming this problem, and maintaining continuity of thought, is to use a cascaded design. In this plan of organization, the major categories of content are set forth first in serial order, each major category being so organized as to most logically lead into the next category. Then the sequence is refined. Each major category is cited again and further differentiated into subcategories—the differentiation being performed in the best possible sequence to yield optimal commonality between subcategories in the sequence. In turn, if necessary, the subcategories are sequentially further refined and elaborated. At each step in the process, the amount of information presented is sufficiently restricted to facilitate reception with minimal cognitive strain. A diagram of cascaded chain sequences is shown in Figure 14. As an example of this process suppose a lesson on the evolution of higher animals is to be taught. One way of doing this is to describe the major phylogenetic steps from simple acoelomic groups through the vertebrates. This constitutes the first chain of major categories, symbolized by R in Series 1 Figure 14. Then each phylogenetic step is analyzed in greater detail to present the morphological and biochemical characteristics which describe each group. This constitutes Series 2 shown in Figure 14. The r's are equivalent to the more detailed descriptions of each major

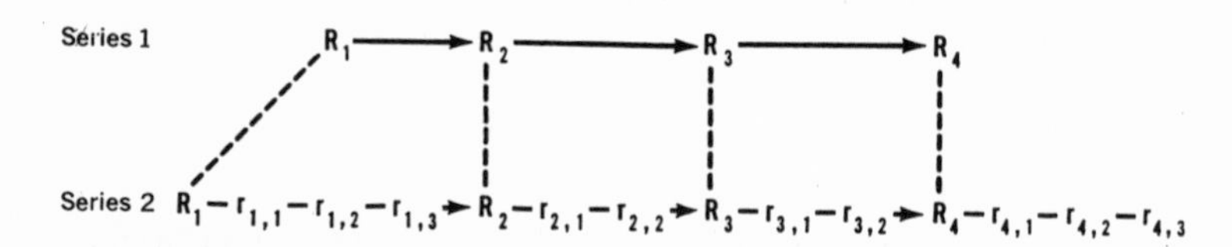

Figure 14 A Cascade Chain Model
The model consists of two series. Major categories are presented in Series 1, then each major category is elaborated in Series 2 in an associated sub-category.

phylogenetic group. Of course, to maintain maximal serial commonality in organization, the similarities of each pair of categories should be cited. In the first series this should be done in general terms and in the final series in more specific terms. One should clearly distinguish between a cascaded chain design and the use of advance organizers as proposed by Ausubel. There are similarities between the two designs. Advance organizers are general conceptual descriptions of a field of study which precede the presentation of relevant, although not identical, specific facts. In a cascaded chain design, the sequence of general categories presented first is a statement of the ideas to be presented in greater detail in the next series. The difference lies partly in the degree of generality of the advance material and partly in the fact that the cascaded design requires parallel development of each series. Thus, the order used in presenting the major categories in the first series must be duplicated in the second, more elaborate series. Strict sequential parallel organization is preferred since the major categories presented in the first series have maximum capacity for sequestering the associated specifics when they are given in the same order in the second series.

An alternative design to a cascaded chain is an advance organizer. The advance organizer is, however, an example of a cluster-centered presentation. The multiple relationships and highly general integration of several concepts used in the advance organizer require its classification as a cluster sequence. One may therefore organize a lesson to begin with a cluster segment (advance organizer) and then proceed into a more conventional serial sequence where new specific facts are presented in a linear fashion.

Principles and Concepts as Themes

Continuity of verbal material can be produced by identifying a central principle or concept to which specific ideas can be related as a lesson or portion thereof unfolds. The principle or concept forms a theme—a thread of an idea which runs throughout the lesson, conferring commonality among the statements. Using themes as a focus for organizing linear sequences of material has the following advantages:

1. A theme helps the teacher maintain a high-structure sequence since the theme is an easily identifiable integrating thought to which new ideas can be sequentially related.
2. Pupil knowledge acquisition is enhanced since the pupils have a constant defining characteristic to supply commonality among new thoughts acquired in a series.
3. Moreover, a theme is a parsimonious way of achieving commonality (continuity) among ideas since it can be applied when necessary to give connectedness to otherwise diverse ideas.

These conclusions are based on structural analyses of classroom communications. It was found that lesson sequences having high commonality (a high B_1 as explained in the section on a biopsychological theory) tend to have a high RAC, indicating the presence of a theme, whereas those lesson segments with low commonality usually do not have a theme (Anderson 1971). Moreover, Trindade (1970) has shown that high-structure lessons organized around various themes yield greater pupil knowledge acquisition than lessons on the same topic where the themes have been disorganized and the structure consequently reduced. Themes can vary in their generality. At the lowest level of abstraction, a theme may be simply an object, category, or group of objects whose properties are presented by constantly alluding to the general class being described. At a higher level of abstraction, a process may be used as the integrating idea conferring commonality. Or, at a still higher level, concepts and principles, such as the concept of the cell as a unit of structure and function, or the principle of feedback control, can be used to tie together the sequential organization of content. The Biological Sciences Curriculum Study has identified nine unifying themes used in their various text books (Schwab). The themes are listed here without further elaboration.

1. Change of living things through time: evolution
2. Diversity of type and unity of pattern in living things
3. The genetic continuity of life
4. The complementarity of organism and environment
5. The biological roots of behavior
6. The complementarity of structure and function
7. Regulation and homeostasis: preservation of life in the face of change
8. Science as enquiry
9. The history of biological conceptions.

A theme, regardless of its level of abstraction, should be sufficiently related to the specifics being taught to allow frequent citation of relationships between the theme and each specific. If the content does not lend itself to identification of principles

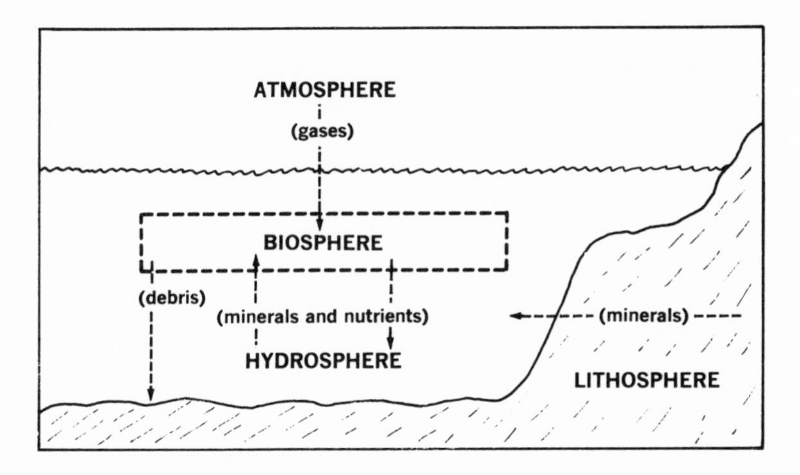

Figure 15 The Marine Environment
The model illustrates relationships among biotic and non-living factors in a marine environment.

or concepts as themes, other mechanisms such as explanatory models may be used to produce lesson commonality.

Models as Themes

Some topics can best be taught as related to a general model. By a model, I mean a scheme, plan, or physical system which integrates each idea to be presented. The model may be a figural, graphic, or verbal presentation of relationships among the ideas to be taught. The model is most logically presented at the beginning of the lesson and used as a point of reference for each specific fact subsequently set forth.

Assume that a lesson is to be taught on marine biology, specifically with reference to the interaction of living things with the non-living environment. One way of introducing this topic is to use the figural model shown in Figure 15.

Each model component is described in terms of its major characteristics. The organization of the biosphere, hydrosphere, lithosphere, and atmosphere is described in general. Then, each component is discussed in greater detail, the relationship of each "sphere" to the biosphere specified, for example. The biosphere consisting of phytoplankton and zooplankton could be described as a community of predators and prey. A general food chain from primary producers to higher order consumers could be cited. Then the exchange of materials between biosphere and hydrosphere—the flow of nutrients, waste products, and gases between the two—might be considered. The exchange of solid waste materials between the biosphere and lithosphere and mineral contributions from the lithosphere could be discussed. Interaction between the biosphere and atmosphere can be presented whereby oxygen, fixed nitrogen as ammonia, and other air borne nutrients are made available to the primary producers in the biosphere. Depth in discussing these individual topics will depend on the maturity of the pupils and the objectives of instruction. Other figural models which can be used to organize sequences of content are:

1. Chemical cycles in the environment
2. Life cycles as generalized diagrams
3. Phylogenetic sequences (evolutionary pathways)
4. Flow charts of physiological, biochemical, and physical changes in living systems
5. Network models: food webs, social interaction patterns among animals, or inhibitory and facilitatory mechanisms among plants in an ecosystem
6. Adaptive grids in genetics
7. Anatomical, tissue, and cellular models

There is obvious educational value in using graphic material (mathematical graphs and symbologies) in conjunction with figural models as a means of helping the student to increase his capacity to organize ideas in abstract ways. The teacher, moreover, will find that the process of constructing models to be used in serial learning is useful for getting his own ideas ordered.

Hierarchies

A hierarchy is an array of ideas stratified so that subordinate ideas are subsumed within higher order ideas. We have already

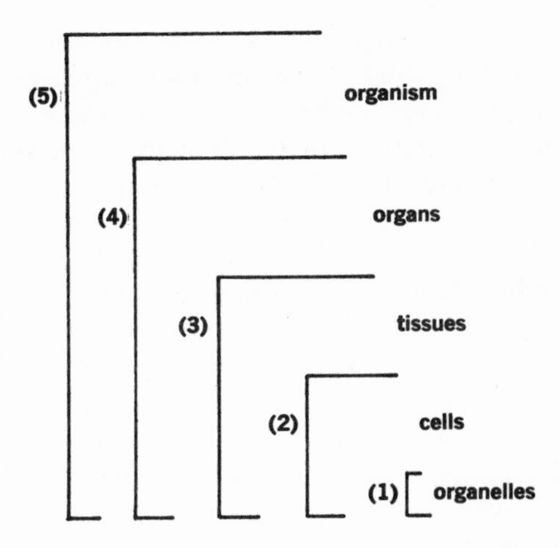

Figure 16 A Hierarchy of Biological Organization
The figure illustrates a five-level hierarchy of biological organization.

discussed Gagné's use of hierarchies in teaching principles and problem-solving skills. A hierarchy may also be used to organize less abstract content in a systematic and psychologically sound way. A hierarchy theoretically enhances serial learning since the most concrete or basic content is presented first followed by more inclusive subsuming content. Moreover, since lower order strata in the hierarchy are subsumed within higher order strata, there is commonality among the various strata. A lesson organized in a hierarchical sequence therefore has a periodic pattern which enhances reception learning. There are several examples of biological content which can be easily organized into hierarchical arrays. The various levels of biological structure as shown in Figure 16 form a nested array. The evolutionary development of structures, some physiological processes, and reproductive processes are examples of other hierarchically ordered events. In each of these cases, lower order characteristics have been incorporated and elaborated upon in higher order characteristics. As a specific example in evolution, sexual reproduction can be traced through stages of isogamy, anisogamy, oogamy, and oogamy within specialized reproductive structures.

Haskell (1970) has published a very remarkable hierarchy as

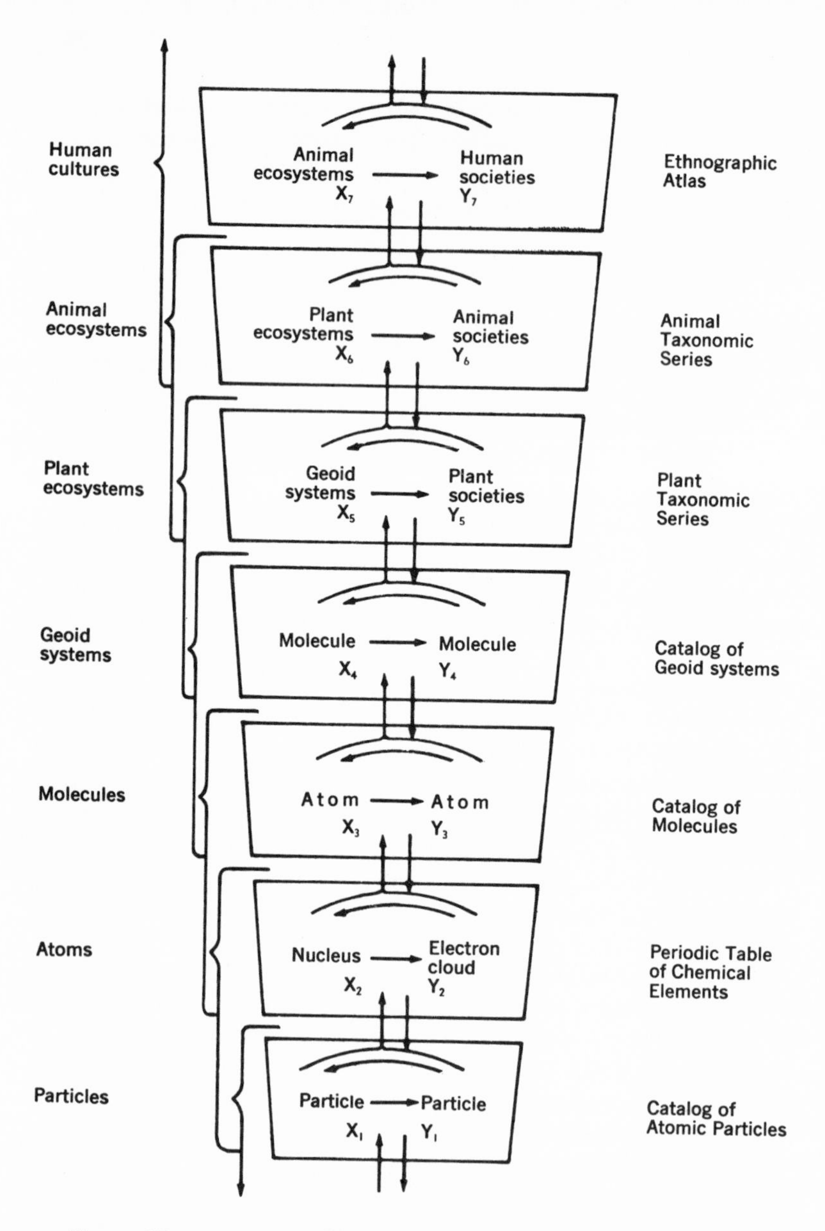

Figure 17 A Hierarchy of Living Things and Their Origin in Non-Living Matter

Arrows within each stratum show interactions giving rise to the next stratum. Each higher order stratum subsumes and expands upon strata beneath (after Haskell 1970).

a curriculum outline wherein biological systems are nested within one another beginning at the atomic level and culminating in social orders. His plan (Figure 17) is clearly a grand scale example of the devices that can be used to organize content in nested arrays.

SEQUENCES BASED ON THE EIGHT CELL COORDINATE MODEL

The eight cell coordinate model described in Chapter One can be used to systematically plan the sequential organization of lesson content. Each cell in the model prescribes a way of organizing material for a segment of a lesson. The sequential development of a lesson can be planned by using various linear conbinations of the cells to describe the over-all organizational plan of the sequence. Thus a lesson may be planned to move from cell 5 to 3 to 2; that is, from specific structures to general structures to general processes. Alternatively, a lesson may be organized to proceed from cell 2 to 4 to 8; from general processes as constants to processes as variables to specific processes as variables. Assuming that a lesson is to be organized in three steps, there are 56 possible ways of combining the eight cells into sets of three, disregarding their order. If we include all possible permutations, there are six ways of ordering each set of three cells. This means there are $6 \times 56 = 336$ total possible sequential patterns that can be generated using the eight cell model. This allows a considerable amount of flexibility in thinking about lesson organization. The number of steps in the lesson may, in addition, be more or less than three and the total possible number of combinations is altered accordingly. If the lesson contains two steps, there are $2 \times 28 = 56$ possible combinations. If there are four steps, there are $24 \times 70 = 1{,}680$ possible combinations based on the model. Now, obviously, the content to be presented may make some of the sequences unfeasible. The teacher must evaluate the possible choices for appropriateness to content and relevance to the pupil's cognitive development in the content area .

Some of the ways that the model can be used to organize a lesson are: (1) identifying themes for lesson segments, (2) planning lessons using a Gagné hierarchy, and (3) planning lessons

CHART 4 THEMES BASED ON THE EIGHT CELL MODEL

Structure	*Process*
Components of living systems: cell, tissue, organ, and organism	Evolution: diversity of form and function in successive generations; adaptation, natural selection, continuity of form
Classifications: taxonomic, ecological, histological, and anatomical	Growth and reproduction: organization of form and function in development
Life stages: phylogenetic, ontogenetic, and reproductive where no reference is made to process	Energy: assimilation and transformation of various forms of energy
Constructs: inferred categories such as gene, pheromone, population, stimulus threshhold, reaction rate, anoxia, prophage, etc.	Information and control systems: messages and homeostasis regulation of growth, reproduction, and ecological associations
	Interactions: competition and accomodation in cells, tissues, organs, and organisms
	Irritability and activity: sensitivity to environmental stimuli resulting in activity

using advance organizers. The model suggests two broad classes of themes in organizing lesson segments: structures (categories—static descriptions) and processes (time correlated events—dynamic descriptions). Chart 4 summarizes various themes falling within these two classes. An examination of Chart 4 shows that the themes proceed from the specific to general. It is important to clearly recognize that a theme may be a specific component being discussed, thereby providing continuity and commonality in a lesson; or, indeed, a theme may be a very general principle. With reference to the model, if a theme is chosen from the structure class in Chart 4, then the appropriate cells to be considered in further specifying the content organization are cells

1, 3, 5, and 7. If a process theme is chosen, then cells 2, 4, 6, and 8 are to be used in further refining the organization of the lesson segment. A lesson may move from a structure theme to a process theme or vice versa. Care should be taken to provide a rich variety of themes in teaching. A wide variety of specific facts in biology can be taught in the context of the themes presented in Chart 4. Practical experience has shown that pupils prefer lessons containing process themes. To illustrate the use of process themes in presenting specific facts of biology, Chart 4 is expanded here by listing some examples of specific facts that can be taught within the context of each theme.

Evolution

1. Plant and animal classification presented as a phylogenetic sequence; the various phyla and subgroups described in serial order from primitive to complex; processes of adaptation and natural selection are used to explain the variety of form and functión in each group.
2. Plant and animal anatomy presented as an adaptive response to environmental demands; organ structure and function explained as mechanisms favoring organismic survival in the face of environmental pressures. Comparative anatomical data can be organized in a sequence based on probable evolutionary development—simpler organisms compared in structure to more advanced forms.
3. Life cycles and reproductive mechanisms can be taught as adaptive responses of the organism to secure survival. The gradual specialization of reproductive structures, the reduction in numbers of offspring with phylogenetic advancement, and the reduction of the gametophyte during evolution toward higher forms can be evaluated as positive adaptive responses to the environment. Movement from an aquatic to mesophytic environment during evolution can be related to these changes in reproductive mechanisms.
4. Genetics presented as a mechanism for providing variability in form and function thereby generating sufficient diversity in offspring to allow natural selection to proceed.

5. Ecology presented as a system of relationships among plants, animals, and their environment; the mutual influences among biotic and physical factors in the environment which influence evolutionary advance of living forms.
6. Animal behavior presented as a mechanism to coordinate activities of members within a species—to protect their boundaries against invaders, to ensure breeding within a compatible gene pool and hence to favor processes of adaptation, natural selection, and evolutionary advance.

Growth and Reproduction

1. Plant and animal morphology can be presented as a product of development processes. The form and function of organs at maturity and during growth can be compared.
2. Plant and animal physiology can be discussed as regulating growth. Changes in physiological functions during maturation provide interesting topics for discussion, particularly of lower organisms such as amphibia where clear cut changes in form and function take place.
3. Genetic concepts are, of course, readily discussed in the context of growth and regulation of development. The relationship of gene composition to reproduction—the differences in genetic composition of offspring produced by asexual and sexual reproduction; the role of sexual reproduction in providing mechanisms of gene combination—hybridization and unmasking of recessive traits.
4. Changes in animal behavior during development—such as courtship behavior, aggression and cooperation, and communication; effects of reproductive rate on community structure and rearing of offspring.

Energy

1. The role of energy flow in the maintenance of life at the cellular, organ, and organismic level can be discussed. Photosynthesis, respiration, and fermentation are topics subsumed within this theme.
2. The flow of energy in food webs among predator and prey, between plants and animals, and from the environment to living things can be used as a lesson theme.

3. The role of food energy in producing movement and thought in animals; the concept of conservation of energy can be used to link chemical energy in food to mechanical and electrical energy used in movement and thought.

Information and Control Systems

1. Feedback control mechanisms at the cellular, tissue, and organismic level are numerous. Regulation of enzyme activity, the operon concept of genetic regulation of enzyme synthesis, hormone action, regulation of blood pressure, blood sugar, red cell numbers, respiration rate, body temperature, and nerve reflexes are examples of this concept.
2. Genetic continuity from one generation to the next can be discussed as information flow. The mutual interaction of organism and environment—each altering the organization of the other—can be treated as a control process. Changes in environment produced by living things have feedback effects on the kind and quantity of organisms that can exist in the environment.
3. Animal behavior is an information process when it arouses a response in another organism. Maintenance of territories and control of population size can be presented as information exchange and inter-organismic control mechanisms.

Interactions

1. Competition among organisms living in the same community, or interactions between an organism and its environment can be included under this theme. Plant root alterations in soil composition, nutrient cycles such as the nitrogen cycle and CO_2-oxygen cycle, molecular interactions in biosynthetic pathways, and community organization among animals are included here.
2. The complementarity between structure and function of plant and animal organs, the process of organismic adaptation to the environment are interaction concepts.

Irritability and Activity

1. Plant and animal sensory systems and their relationships to action belong in this theme. The integration of visual, auditory, smell, and taste reception with muscular and

glandular activity in animals, and the response of plants to light direction (phototropism), gravity (geotropism), and light and dark cycles (photoperiodism) are included in this theme.

2. Principles of neurophysiology and motor coordination through proprioception can be integrated under this theme.
3. The response of social animals to repel invaders and concerted social activities are examples of social irritability and activity.

The teacher and student benefit by an orderly yet frequent change in themes used in organizing segments of a lesson. If the content is not very abstract, then several themes may be used in close succession to give lesson variety and provide flexibility in pupil knowledge acquisition. If the content is abstract and possibly difficult for the student to follow, then it is wise to organize the content rather consistently around a single theme to reduce cognitive strain and enhance orderly acquisition. However, once the student has gained a clear comprehension of the knowledge, it is useful to encourage divergent ways of thinking about the material. A cluster-centered approach, for example, suggests moving within the context of a theme from constants to variables; generally, from cells 1, 2, 5, or 6 toward cells 3, 4, 7, or 8 in the eight cell model. It is recommended that if the lesson begins with specifics, it should move toward generalities—cells 1 through 4. A Gagné hierarchy is such an example. Specific and highly concrete facts are followed by increasingly inclusive and abstract material as the lesson unfolds. This suggests movement from the lower half of the model to the upper half. The important additional distinction is that the sequence is not merely an orderly well integrated succession of categories but a subsumptive organization wherein the content proceeds toward greater inclusiveness as the lesson unfolds. Examples have been cited in the preceding discussion. The model allows decision making at each level in the hierarchy about structure-process and constant-variable characteristics. One may proceed, for example, from cell 7 to cell 2 in a diagonal path across the model. Another diagonal path leads from cell 8 to cell 2, on the same side of the model.

A lesson, however, based on an advance organizer would clearly proceed in a reverse direction to that constructed for a Gagné hierarchy. The advance organizer, being a highly general and inclusive introduction, necessitates our beginning the lesson in the upper half of the eight cell model and moving toward the lower half. The path chosen in moving from generalities to specifics will be determined by the factual ideas to be subsumed by the advance organizer. For example, the lesson might move from general processes (cell 2 or 4) to general structures (cell 1 or 3), or to specific processes (cell 6 or 8) and finally to specific structures (cell 5 or 7). Other such combinations can be generated by examination of the model in relation to the content to be taught. Chart 5 should be consulted as a source of ideas for advance organizer concepts. It is absolutely essential, as explained in the discussion of subsumption theory, that the advance organizer concepts be logically relevant to the specifics they are supposed to subsume. To familiarize yourself more thoroughly with the eight cell coordinate model, select a chapter in a biology textbook and place each section into one of the cells in the model. This will sometimes require that you abstract the major thrust of each section. If the majority of the statements are generalities then *generalities* would be chosen as the defining characteristic (as opposed to specifics even though a few are cited). You can also map the general flow of organization in the chapter by listing the sequence of cell numbers you have assigned to each section.

Cluster Learning

Cluster learning is the acquisition of multiple relationships among ideas. It includes concept learning and complex network learning where several variables, processes, or structures are interrelated. The content is organized in a branching and cross-linked arrangement. Ideas previously presented are recalled and interrelated with currently presented ideas. The focus of attention is more diffuse than in linear lessons. In this section, we give particular attention to the application of psychological theory to increasing concept learning efficiency. We examine ways of increasing the efficiency of teaching concepts such as adaptation, biogenesis, homeostasis, photoperiodism, taxonomic categories, the cell concept, metabolism, and ecosystem. At appropriate points we appeal to Bruner's study on concept attainment for psychological data supporting teaching strategies. We apply Bruner's study results to the practical problems of teaching concepts, recognizing that the experimental conditions he employed are not identical to the conditions occurring during reception learning.

Teaching of concepts can become a disorderly process unless careful thought is given to the organization of the lesson. A systematic way of approaching the problem is to analyze each concept to determine the attributes needed to specify that concept. An attribute, you will recall, is a quality or property common to items categorized within the concept. Each attribute assigned to the concept must have a value—a specific quality which distinguishes that concept from other concepts. When all relevant attributes have been identified, they should be ordered in a systematic way, perhaps beginning with the simple and progressing to the complex ones. As an example, suppose we are planning to teach the concept of metabolism. We list the attributes and attribute values appropriate for a secondary school biology class.

Attribute	*Attribute Value*
Chemical process	Maintained by biological molecules
Energy production	Chemical, electrical, heat, and mechanical
Life functions	Food digestion, blood circulation, waste excretion, responsiveness, growth
Environmental dependence	Nutrient, water, and air exchange

We plan to teach the concept of metabolism as a chemical process yielding energy in support of life functions. The process of metabolism, moreover, is dependent on the environment for conditions favoring metabolic activity. Each specific quality of each attribute (namely, attribute value) is presented. The question arises how best to organize the presentation to reduce cognitive strain and enhance concept acquisition. Bruner's study suggests that a conservative-focussing strategy is appropriate. Each attribute should be presented, its positive and negative values cited, and examples of instances given. The lesson outline could be organized as follows.

1. Metabolism is a chemical process carried out on the molecular level. (Similarities and differences between biological molecules and non-living molecules are cited. This includes contrasting proteins and mineral molecules, and enzymes and catalysts).
2. Metabolism yields energy—chemical energy as ATP, electrical energy in membrane surfaces, heat energy as body temperature, and mechanical energy as body movement. These forms of energy would be contrasted to the non-living forms encountered in the environment.
3. Life functions are supported by metabolic processes which yield the necessary energy to promote food digestion, blood circulation, waste execretion, irritability, and growth.
4. All of the aforementioned processes are dependent upon interactions with the environment. Each of the prior stated functions is related to nutrient, water, and air supply. The survival of the total organism can be related to the concept of metabolism.

This example illustrates how the application of the conservative-focussing strategy to concept learning allows us to unravel the attributes specific to a concept, order them in a logical sequence, and, by careful individual attribute analysis, set forth the essential properties of the concept. The potentially diffuse hodge-podge of characteristics has been ordered in a linear array without destroying the cluster of ideas subsumed within the concept. Note also that the above example has formed a hierarchy, further facilitating stable and orderly acquisition of the concept. If instead of this orderly conservative-focussing strategy, one had presented the attributes in a mixed fashion, interrelating all of them from start, the student would suffer excessive cognitive strain and acquisition of the concept would be more difficult. Additional examples of cluster-centered lessons are given in Chapter Three. The steps in preparing an outline for a cluster-centered lesson are summarized:

1. Identify essential attributes of the concept or components of the system to be communicated.
2. Order them beginning with the most simple and proceeding to the most complex.
3. List the negative and positive qualities of each, with examples.
4. Where appropriate relate prior learned items in the lesson to newly acquired ones. The interrelationships should be stated only after the newly introduced attribute or component has been firmly established.
5. Conclude the lesson or segment thereof with a general statement interrelating all of the component items previously presented.

Problem Solving

Enlightened biology teachers recognize that effective science teaching includes more than knowledge transmission. Science is indeed a body of knowledge, but it is clearly more than that. Science is a process of analyzing experiences to create models of reality as a way of explaining, predicting, and further exploring empirical experiences. Sometimes textbooks reduce scientific processes of investigation to a few statements of procedure. For example, a condensed list of the scientific method might be: (1) identify or sense a problem, (2) state a hypothesis, (3) design a controlled experiment, and (4) evaluate the results and accept or reject the hypothesis. Although the list gives some fundamental steps in experiment design, we now recognize that such lists are often naively simple and misleading. The role of theory, various methods of problem solving, intuitive judgments, and creative thinking are neglected. Moreover, the list implies that scientific investigations are all of the controlled-experiment type. Descriptive studies, such as those performed in natural history and some ecological field studies, are clearly scientific in their orderly search for empirical evidence and their creative analysis of data. Some experimental studies are often very elegant and ingenious in design. Their complexity and precision in testing hypotheses should be recognized as one part of scientific procedure. The use of descriptive techniques and creative interpretations of data based on rational judgments should also be recognized as part of scientific investigation. The purpose of this section is to set forth some aids in recognizing basic problem-solving skills students can acquire during enquiry-oriented classroom lessons. We explore some of the difficulties pupils may encounter in learning problem solving. Suggestions from psychological studies are made to help ameliorate these difficulties. The term enquiry in this book means the kind of open-ended, problem-oriented experiences recommended by Schwab (1963) to introduce students to processes of scientific investigation and to scientists as scholars. We discuss ways of teaching problem solving through reception learning, discussion, and laboratory experiences. Finally, some suggestions are made, based on psychological studies, to overcome difficulties in problem solving and enhance student problem-solving skills.

Reception learning (lecture) need not be restricted to knowledge acquisition. Properly organized lectures containing summaries of research studies at a level appropriate to the maturity of the student greatly enhance his appreciation of and preparation for problem solving. At appropriate points in the lecture, the teacher should take time to point out the possible cognitive skills used by the scientist in performing his study. The categories cited in Chapter One under cognitive skill objectives, taken from Bloom's *Taxonomy of Educational Objectives*, are very useful in preparing such a lecture. The teacher can point out places in the study where the scientist *translated* his data into mathematical formulas or presented them in graph form. *Extrapolation* from theory (hypotheses) or from previous descriptive data, *analysis* of components or broad organization schemes within the data, *application* of methods or principles of science, *synthesis* of a new theory, *plan* of experiment or model to explain observations, and *evaluation* of data should be given when appropriate. Sometimes, after several lessons of this kind, it is wise to ask for student analysis of the described experiment using these categories. Thus the teacher demonstrates the analysis and then encourages the student in subsequent lessons to perform the same kind of analyses. Certainly the student should be given the opportunity to suggest alternative ways of interpreting the scientist's data, to extrapolate where the scientist did not, and to evaluate significance and accuracy. The student should come to see the dangers in extrapolating trends when insufficient data are available to do so reliably.

Some attention can be given to the role of theory, hypothesis-stating, and experiment-testing in lectures. The student needs to know that a theory is more than a "tentative and abstract explanation of reality that has not been proven." This naive definition, so frequently presented in textbooks, may confuse the learner who subsequently encounters a more general use of the concept in scientific literature. A theory may be described as an explanation of experience wherein principles and concepts representing scientific observations are logically related to one another in a systematic way. A theory frequently is a statement which correlates and organizes previously incoherent and isolated observations. The scientific value of a theory is judged in terms of its internal consistency and its correct use of logic in integrating principles and concepts through causal and explanatory statements. A theory may indeed be a tentative explanation of reality, but also should be testable through evaluation of hypotheses drawn from the theory. A hypothesis is a prediction of relationships between two or more variables. Thus, the hypothesis may predict, based on a theory, that event x will cause event y; or that events x and y will vary together or separately in some predictable way. In a statement of hypothesis, the event to be varied during testing is called the independent variable; the event to be observed and assessed as an effect of the independent variable is called the dependent variable. The relationship should be stated in a way that allows reliable observational or logical verification. Causal relations can be tested by seeking the following kinds of evidence: if x is a cause of y, then x must precede y in time, and x should vary concomitantly with y, and within the experimental situation no other variable should be identifiable as an equally possible cause of y.

As an example, consider the following familiar situation in plant physiology. Plant stems are known to bend toward a source of visible light. This behavior of positive phototropism can be explained as a product of hormone action. Assume that a growth hormone is produced in the apex of plant stems. The hormone enhances stem cell elongation. Translocation of the hormone from stem apex downward brings it in contact with growing cells. Under conditions of uniform illumination, all of the cells elongate at a uniform rate. Now assume that the hormone is photolabile or sensitive to light in such a way it no longer functions when illuminated. The side of a stem receiving illumination will not elongate as much as the non-illuminated side. The differential rate of growth causes the stem to bend toward the light. This can rightly be called a theory since it interrelates several observations and scientific concepts through explanatory statements. Thus, stem bending toward light is explained as an effect of differential stem growth produced by uneven distribution of hormone within the stem.

The theory can be tested at several levels. If there is a growth hormone, it should be isolatable. The isolated hormone verifies a basic assumption. If the hormone is produced in the stem apex, then removal of its apex should prevent the stem from bending toward illumination. In this hypothesis, the independent variable is the presence or absence of a stem apex. The dependent variable is stem bending in response to light. Additional hypotheses can be suggested. If the hypotheses are tested through a carefully controlled experiment, verification of the hypotheses supports the theory, negation concurrently questions the strength of the theory as a predictor. Schwab has invented some clever classroom presentations called "Invitations to Enquiry" which illustrate scientific problem solving and also elicit student participation. You may want to create your own enquiry lessons by delving into scientific journals to find research reports appropriate to illustrate scientific problem solving.

Discussion groups can be used effectively in science classrooms to develop group problem-solving skills. The material chosen for discussion is important in determining the success of the experience. The material should provide a context for evaluation of evidence and interpretation of results. Suitable discussion materials include articles on competing theories, and models or interpretations of findings. For example, articles on Darwinian, Lamarckian, and catastrophist theories of species origin can be used to stimulate discussion on evolution. Current articles on social issues related to technology (applied biology, medicine, eugenics, and agriculture) often provide useful materials. Whatever material is chosen should provide a rich source of varied interpretations, but also should be amenable to verification of conclusions by citation of scientific evidence rather than dogma or opinion. To prepare the group for discussion, materials should be distributed well in advance so the student can become thoroughly familiar with them before coming to class. One may choose to use a laboratory period for the discussion. The discussion itself can be organized in one of three ways.

1. The group may suggest key issues to be discussed. These are listed on the chalkboard in an order most conducive to a systematic discussion.
2. An "issue nominating" group can be appointed to preview the material and suggest key issues to be discussed. These are appended to the reading materials distributed to the class. The discussion centers largely around the preselected issues.
3. Several student panels (groups of two or three students) begin discussion by clearly stating the issues or positions presented in each paper. The whole group can then address itself to these issues.

The teacher should be alert to keep the discussions on a scientific basis by suggesting that evidence be rational, empirical, and consistent with verified principles and theories in the discipline. Group discussions lend themselves to development of general problem-solving skills. The student should be aware of general principles of evaluating theories, analyzing data, and distinguishing between opinions and conclusions based on data. To further promote divergent or creative thinking, the teacher may divide the class into small groups, allowing each one to develop its own critical analysis of the problem. The findings of each group could then be presented by the group leaders to the entire class. In all of the aforementioned instances, the teacher does well to serve as a guide and participant in discussion sessions rather than as overseer of the conversation.

Laboratory tasks provide an excellent opportunity for pupils to gain cognitive skills as well as manual facility with laboratory procedures. Modern laboratory investigations for secondary schools emphasize problem-solving approaches rather than descriptive tasks. Skills in gathering data, suggesting explanations for observations, and developing plans for testing hypotheses drawn from these explanations have become widely used in modern curricula. (See Biological Sciences Curriculum Study.) The teacher is encouraged to participate indirectly in helping the student discover answers to his problems rather than giving direct and formal instruction on each step to be used in the problem-solving task. However, practical experience shows that some teacher assistance in helping the student formulate reasonable questions and attend to potentially useful data, among the often bewildering array available, is warranted. Particularly early in such experiences, the student may need some teacher assistance through verbal interaction. A few well directed questions can help the student begin gathering data and recognize alternative explanations for his observations.

For the teacher who has some difficulty in conceptualizing the kinds of procedural errors pupils are likely to make in problem solving, some pertinent research is cited and practical applications made to classroom experiences. Bloom and Broder (1950) performed a clever study on problem-solving among college students. Although they used verbal problems as the source of their data, the errors and limitations they discovered in student initiation and completion of problem-solving tasks have relevance for open-ended laboratory and discussion tasks. Bloom and Broder began with the assumption that the best way to study problem-solving was to follow the actual course of thought used in solving problems. They asked each subject to verbalize as much of his thought as possible while solving the test problems. The problems were multiple response questions similar to those on achievement examinations. They were all content questions dealing with problems in the scholarly disciplines. Bloom and Broder recognized that the methods used to assess mental processes were relatively crude since only a part of the total thought sequence was verbalized by each subject. Nonetheless, they were able to identify certain characteristics exhibited by successful problem solvers. Four categories of responses to problem-solving tasks were identified:

1. Understanding the nature of the problem
2. Understanding of the ideas contained in the problem
3. General approach to solving the problem
4. Attitude toward the solution of problems

Each category is described in detail and application made to laboratory problem solving.

Understanding the nature of the problem. Successful problem solvers were able to identify or classify the problem as a particular kind. They were able to identify key elements or phrases which allowed them to begin an attack on the problem. They generally were skilled in reducing the mass of data into several clearly recognizable categories which allowed them to decide about techniques most appropriate to the task. Non-successful problem solvers seemed unable to comprehend the kind of problem involved or to identify the parts of it which might be most conducive to analysis.

Understanding the idea contained in the problem. Successful problem solvers were able to mobilize information necessary to complete the problem. They were able to draw out the implications of the problem, thereby establishing links with previously acquired knowledge. The non-successful subjects were equally knowledgeable in many cases, but were unable to systematically call forth the information needed to complete the problem. When the experimenter prodded, these subjects often were able to recall the essential information. Also, when given some cues about inferences drawn from statements in the problem, or ways of forming new categories of data, these subjects sometimes succeeded in completing the problem.

General approach to solving the problems. The successful subjects differed from non-successful subjects in three ways: (1) extent of thought about the problem; (2) care and system in thinking about the problem; and (3) ability to follow through on a process of reasoning. The successful problem solvers took time to develop a hypothesis or plausible explanation of the facts presented. They attempted to follow through on these assumptions until the results showed promise of being correct or, conversely, incorrect. A new assumption was established and a new approach to the problem was initiated and worked through to a logical conclusion. The non-successful subjects jumped around from one approach to another without following through on one approach to a final conclusion. The non-successful subjects failed to complete a logical line of argument. They might get half way through a logical argument and then stop, seemingly having lost the general perspective which initiated the plan.

Attitude toward the solution of problems. Successful problem solvers took a positive view of the probability of their completing the task. They recognized the value of logical reasoning in finding solutions to problems. Non-successful subjects made global assessments of the problem deciding at the outset either that they could do the problem or not. They seemed reticent to apply logical analyses to problems they assessed as being beyond them or impossible to accomplish.

Students who have difficulty completing laboratory projects to their own satisfaction may suffer from some of the aforementioned limitations. To allow these students to continuously suffer defeat is hardly a reasonable approach to developing a healthy understanding of the processes of science. Therefore, at times the teacher needs to intervene in a laboratory experience when the student is having obvious difficulty in making a rational start. I have seen secondary school biology laboratories in which the teacher was committed to complete nonintervention during an open-ended investigation. The bitter frustration of a student sometimes erupted in destructive or nonsensical completion of the task. The results of the Bloom and Broder study give the teacher some clues as to the kinds of skills floundering students need to develop in order to become successful problem solvers. The wise teacher intervenes as unobtrusively as possible to help floundering students by asking appropriate questions to direct their attention to the following factors.

1. What are the important components of the problem? What are the key differences between various parts of the problem that might give a clue about where to begin the problem?
2. What previous information have you gained about this? What did your text or laboratory manual or special reading assignment say about that? Have you had any previous experiences which might suggest the reason for an observation or an explanation?
3. Do you have any suggestions as to the possible solutions to the problem? What hypotheses or assumptions about the solution do you have? Have you carefully followed through on that assumption?

A general tone of confidence in helping the student identify and follow through on logical reasoning processes no doubt increases his capacity to do so in the future. A teacher who is aware of the above-stated blocks to problem solving soon comes to recognize those students who need some systematic assistance in overcoming their deficiency. It is generally wise on the first several occasions to ask rather direct questions to get the student to begin the process of asking appropriate questions and recalling data in a calm and rational way. On subsequent occasions, the teacher does well to be less directive and ask the student to recall the behavior pattern he used on prior occasions. Eventually, the pupil can be placed in groups with other successful problem solving students where their systematic approach reinforces his own behavior and gives him confidence to pursue the tasks in a logical and orderly manner. It is very important for the teacher to take time to analyze the students in his class, to develop a systematic way of helping them in individual problem-solving tasks, and then of moving them gradually into groups where their progress will be supported. A student who is thrust too soon into an active and aggressive group of problem solvers may lose essential confidence in his ability to maintain the systematic patterns of analysis the teacher has helped him acquire. It is very important, moreover, to provide opportunities for all students to exhibit creative and innovative solutions to problems of their own choice. Some laboratory sessions should be devoted to these student-initiated projects where they gain confidence in thinking creatively.

Chapter Three

THE ORGANIZATION OF MODERN IDEAS OF BIOLOGY

The general principles of lesson organization discussed in Chapter Two are illustrated now in a series of sample lessons. Each lesson is organized using a modern biology theme as an integrating idea. In some cases the lessons are more highly structured than is normally the case in written presentations. This is done intentionally, to illustrate organization appropriate for oral presentation. Each sample lesson is organized in a way that illustrates some principle or combination of principles cited in Chapters One and Two. After each lesson is presented, an analysis of its organization is given. The objectives of the sample lesson are set forth and the rationale underlying the organization of the lesson is described. The content of the lessons is presented at a fairly general and fundamental level suitable for use in high school lesson planning. The purpose of the sample lessons is to illustrate some principles of teaching more than to increase your sophistication in content knowledge. I trust, however, that the unique organization of the sample lessons, and in some cases the novelty of the material, will stimulate your interest and increase your fund of basic knowledge.

The first two lessons are on the same topic. The organization of the first is serial-centered; the second one is organized in a cluster-centered mode. This allows a comparative analysis of the two lesson structures. Each lesson is analyzed at its conclusion and then the two are compared to highlight their similarities and differences in organization. The topic of the two lessons is nucleic acids as information carrying molecules, a basic idea of molecular biology. For purposes of identification during analysis, each tenth statement of the lesson is numbered with a superscript.

Lesson One Information-Carrying Molecules: The Nucleic Acids

The living cell is a remarkable assemblage of molecules serving many different functions. One group of molecules called nucleic acids has the function of storing and transmitting information in the cell. The nucleic acids have the capacity to hold information by the kinds of molecules linked in the nucleic acid. We can think of the nucleic acids as code sequences very much like Morse code of telegraphy. The dots and dashes of Morse code can be translated into words which carry information. In the living cell, the nucleic acid molecular sequence carries information about the organization of cell activities and the production of new structural molecules for the synthesis of cellular organelles. The structure of some nucleic acids is described. We build up the structure of the molecules from the most simple components to the complete complex molecule.

At the simplest level, nucleic acids are composed of molecules called nitrogenous bases. A nitrogenous base is a ring compound containing carbon, hydrogen, nitrogen, and oxygen.[10] There are two kinds of bases, pyrimidines and purines. A pyrimidine ring has two nitrogen atoms linked in a hexagonal ring.

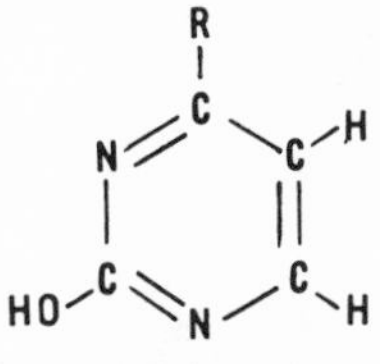

pyrimidine

Purines are more complex. They contain two rings. One of the rings is a pyrimidine and the other one is a five-membered ring containing nitrogen and carbon.

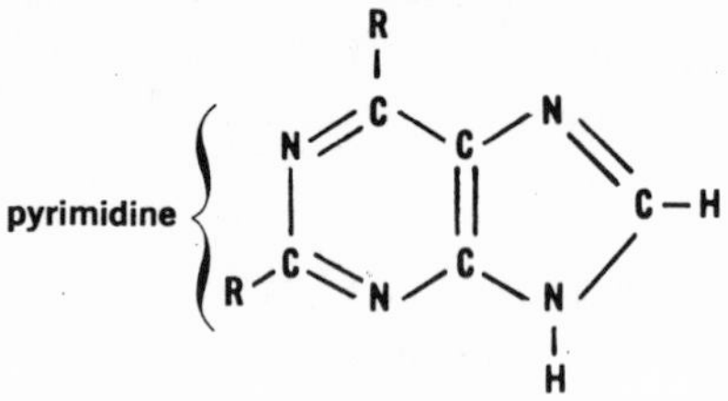

pyrimidine

purine

The atoms attached to the pyrimidine ring determine its nature. There are three kinds of pyrimidine molecules. The three pyrimidine molecules are cytosine, uracil, and thymine. You can see that each one has a particular arrangement for the nitrogen, oxygen, and/or carbon atoms attached to the ring.

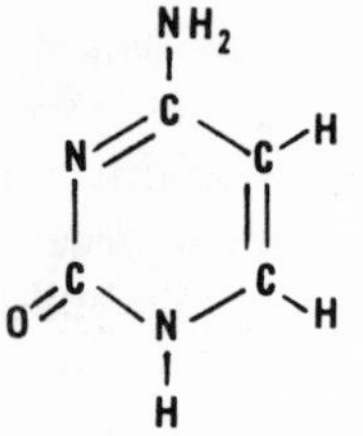

cytosine

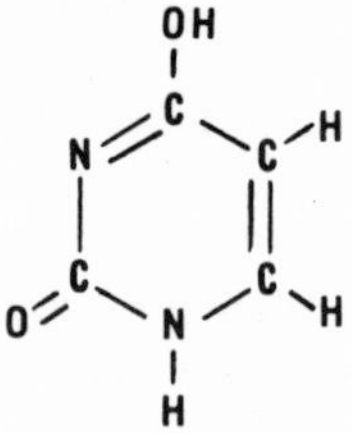

uracil

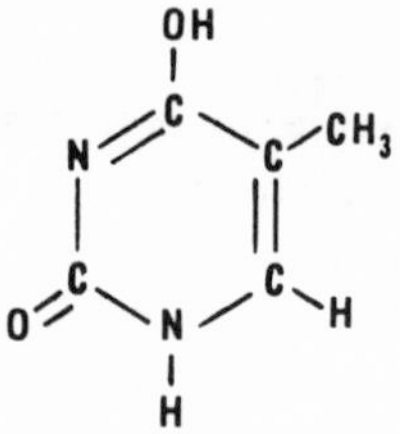

thymine

There are two kinds of purines, based on the arrangement of attached nitrogen and oxygen atoms.

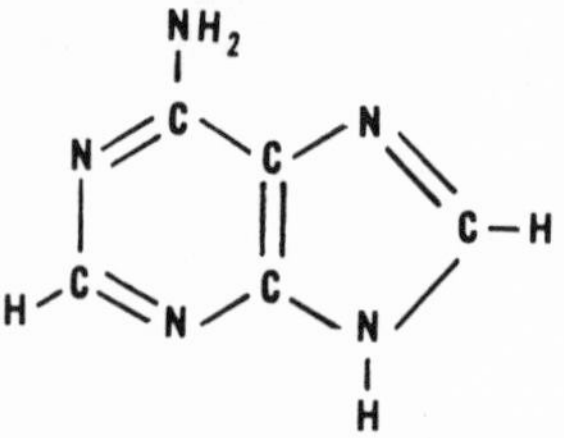

adenine

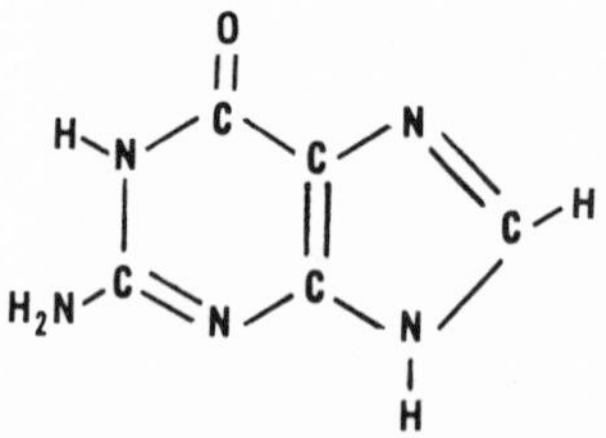

guanine

A nitrogen atom is attached to the purine ring in adenine.[20] Guanine has a nitrogen and an oxygen attached to its purine ring.

In the next step in building a nucleic acid molecule, we examine how the bases are attached to a sugar molecule called ribose. Each pyrimidine and purine molecule is linked to a five-carbon sugar called ribose.

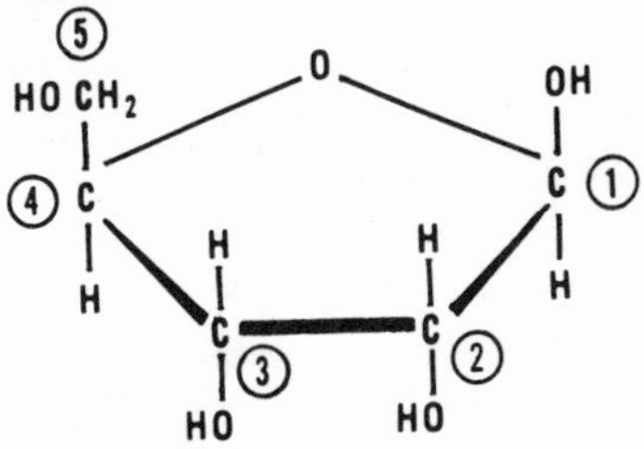

ribose

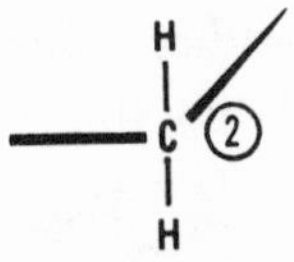

deoxyribose

The carbon atoms in the ribose molecule are numbered from right to left as shown. There are two kinds of ribose molecules—deoxyribose and ribose. The difference between the two is the kind of atom attached to the second carbon atom. Ribose contains a hydroxyl group, whereas deoxyribose contains a hydrogen at the second carbon atom. The name deoxyribose implies a ribose without an oxygen. The ribose molecule is attached to a purine or pyrimidine ring at the number one carbon atom.

pyrimidine

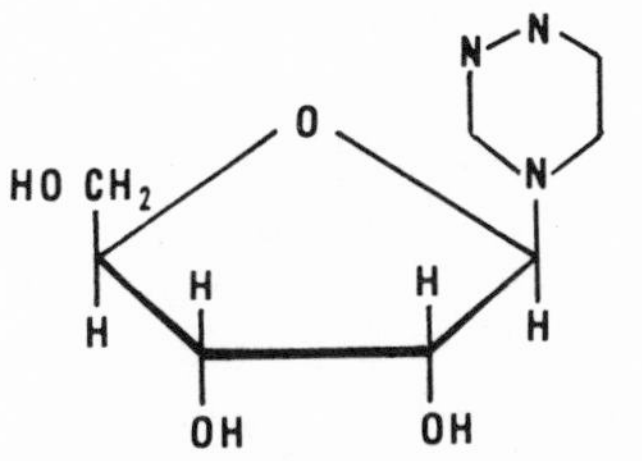

purine

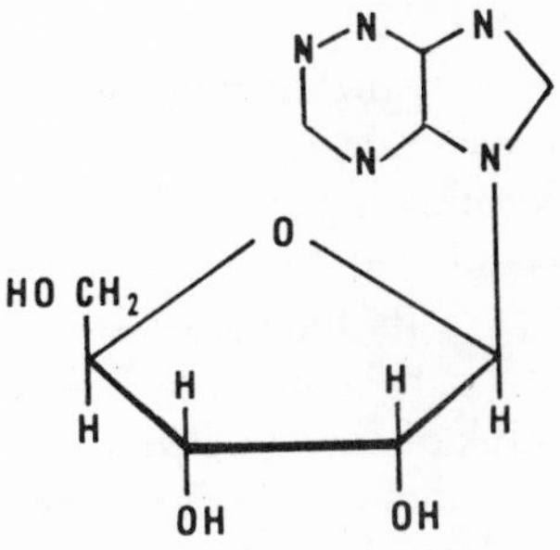

nucleosides

Note that the pyrimidine and purine molecules are attached through a covalent bond to the carbon atom.[30] A molecule composed of a purine and ribose or a pyrimidine and ribose is called a nucleoside. The particular name of a nucleoside depends on the kind of nitrogenous base linked to the ribose. There are two purine nucleosides, adenosine and guanosine, containing, respectively, adenine and guanine bases. The pyrimidine nucleosides of importance in this discussion are cytidine, uridine, and thymidine, containing, respectively, cytosine, uracil, and thymine nitrogenous bases. The kind of sugar molecule, whether deoxyribose or ribose, makes a difference as to bases linked to it. Guanine and adenine are linked with either deoxyribose or ribose. Cytosine is linked with either kind of ribose. Uracil, however, is linked only with ribose, and thymine is linked only with deoxyribose.

Bases linked to ribose	*Bases linked to deoxyribose*
adenine	adenine
guanine	guanine
cytosine	cytosine
uracil	thymine

A nucleoside is further built up to form a nucleotide. A nucleotide is a nucleoside with a phosphate group attached to the fifth carbon atom of the ribose.[40] The phosphate is linked to the carbon atom by an ester linkage. An ester linkage is a bond between an alcohol group and an acid. A nucleotide is produced when phosphoric acid forms an ester linkage with the alcohol group on the fifth carbon of the nucleoside ribose. The ester linkage is called a phospho-ester linkage since a phosphate group participates. The main distinguishing characteristic, therefore, between a nucleoside and a nucleotide is the presence of a phosphate group forming a phospho-ester linkage. Now, you should clearly understand that the kind of base associated with a nucleotide determines its biological specificity. By biological specificity I mean the particular code function that a molecule performs. We can think of each nucleotide as a code letter. The kind of nitrogenous base determines the information specificity of the nucleotide. It is obvious that one nucleotide differs from another only in the kind of purine or pyrimidine base associated with it.[50] We see that the nucleotides become linked to form sequences of three. Each group of three nucleotides forms a code word. Before we consider this further, we examine how the nucleotides become linked to one another to form a long molecule. All nucleotides contain a phosphate group on the fifth carbon.

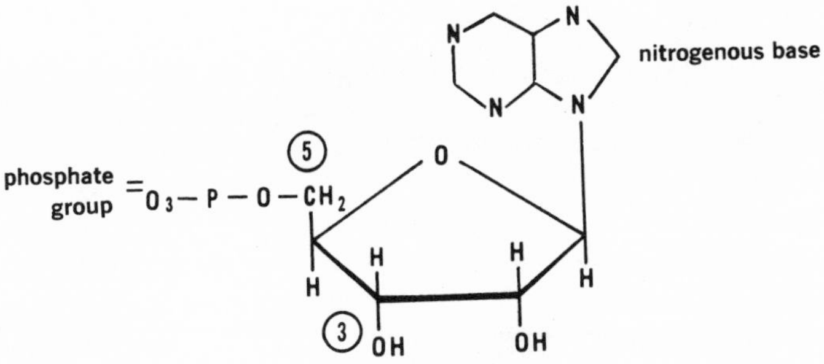

nitrogenous base

phosphate group $^{=}O_3-P-O-CH_2$

nucleotide

They also contain a hydroxyl group on the third carbon. Now it is possible for two nucleotides to link to form a dinucleotide. The phosphate group of one nucleotide forms an ester linkage with the hydroxyl group on carbon three of a second nucleotide.

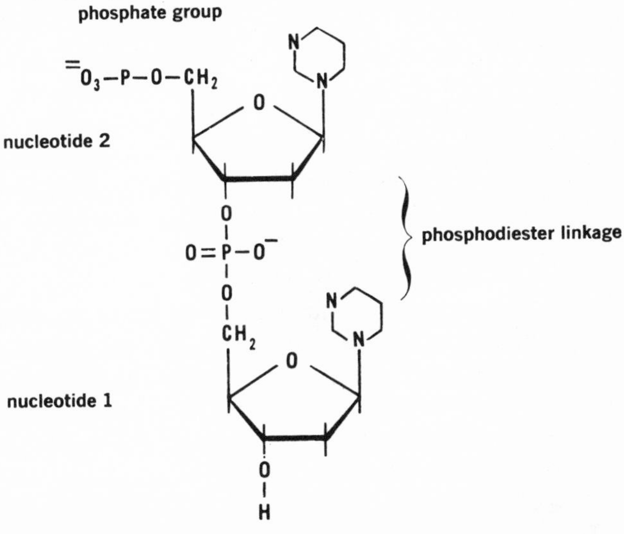

phosphate group

nucleotide 2

phosphodiester linkage

nucleotide 1

The ester linkage is called a phosphodiester linkage since the phosphate group links two nucleotides. The prefix *di* means, of course, two. We have two linkages of an ester type formed by one phosphate group.[60] Therefore, it is very logical to call the linkage a phosphodiester linkage. In the same way it makes sense to call the two linked molecules a dinucleotide since there are two nucleotide molecules linked together.

Now, what is a polynucleotide? A polynucleotide is a molecule made up of many nucleotides in sequence. It is a very large molecule containing often hundreds of nucleotides. A polynucleotide gets its name from the fact that there are numerous nucleotides in sequence. The Greek prefix for many is *poly*. Polynucleotide means many nucleotides. A polynucleotide is characterized by the kinds of purines and pyrimidines associated with its nucleotide subunits. There are many possible polynucleotide sequences, depending on the pattern of linkage and kind of nucleotides present.[70] In addition, there are two kinds of polynucleotide molecules. Those polynucleotide molecules containing deoxyribose in their nucleotides are called DNA strands. DNA is an abbreviation for deoxyribonucleic acid. The letters D, N, and A are the key letters in the word *d*eoxyribo*n*ucleic *a*cid. The other kind of polynucleotide is RNA. These letters stand for ribonucleic acid. RNA polynucleotides are strands of nucleotides containing ribose sugar molecules. RNA and DNA also differ in the presence of different bases on their sugar groups as explained earlier. RNA contains uracil and DNA contains thymine. Otherwise, RNA and DNA are comparable.[80] Thus, the distinguishing characteristics to keep in mind are that RNA has a ribose sugar and uracil and DNA has a deoxyribose sugar and thymine. DNA is usually found in the nucleus and RNA is found in the cytoplasm of cells.

DNA strands can form a double helix by cross linkage between the bases in two parallel strands. Thus each strand contains nucleosides linked by phosphates making them a polynucleotide. Each nucleotide in the polynucleotide has a base projecting outward from it in space. We may think of the phosphate groups and sugar groups as the backbone of the polynucleotide and the bases as potential cross linkages projecting out in space. Two polynucleotide strands form a double helix by base pair linkages. The base adenine links specifically with thymine, and guanine links specifically with cytosine. Therefore we get a series of cross linkages by interaction of specific pairs of bases.[90] The specific association between two bases is due to the pattern of oxygen and hydrogen atoms on the base molecules. Oxygen and hydrogen can form a bridge between two molecules. The bridge is called a hydrogen bond. The hydrogen bond forms only if the oxygen and hydrogen are in close spatial relation to one another. Adenine attracts thymine and guanine attracts cytosine because their respective oxygen and hydrogen atoms are closely apposed to one another when two polynucleotides line up side by side.

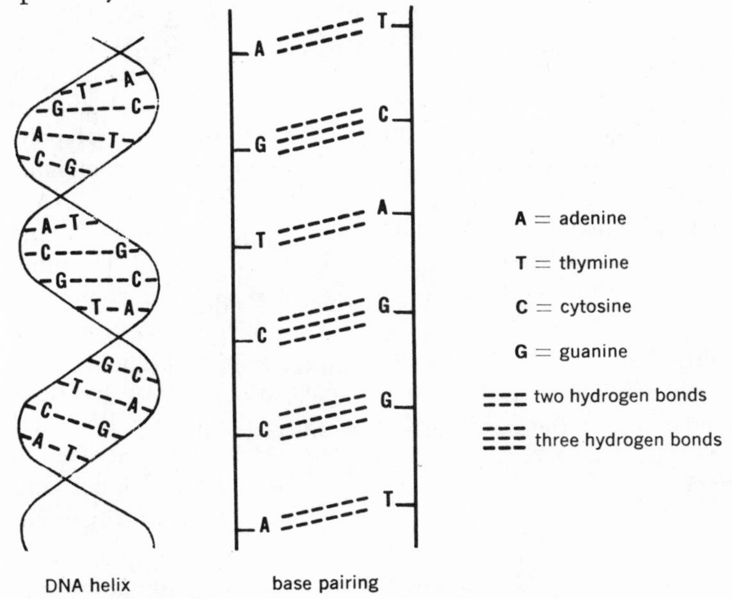

An adenine does not usually pair with a guanine, nor a thymine with a uracil since such pairs do not form stable hydrogen bonds. The double helix is characteristic of DNA molecules and is stabilized by the hydrogen bonds cross linking the strands.

RNA molecules are usually smaller than DNA molecules. RNA usually does not form a long double helix. Both DNA and RNA, however, contain the same basic components: purines, pyrimidines, ribose molecules, nucleosides, and nucleotides.[100] The particular atomic composition of these molecules and their spatial arrangement determines whether the polynucleotide is DNA or RNA.

Now, how do polynucleotides store and transmit information? We know that the sequence of nucleotides in a DNA molecule determines the kind of protein made in a cell. The DNA strand is composed of groups of three nucleotides. Each group of three can specify a particular part of a protein molecule called an amino acid. If we examine the linear sequence of a DNA molecule we see a pattern, such as AAA GCG AAC TTT GTG. Each segment of three bases represents a part of a protein molecule. How then does the information in the DNA code become translated into proteins? This is a process involving DNA, RNA, and protein synthesizing sites in the cytoplasm. Two kinds of RNA are necessary for the direction of protein biosynthesis.[110] These are messenger RNA and transfer RNA. Messenger RNA is a relatively large RNA molecule. It is produced by the DNA in a cell nucleus. Messenger RNA moves from the nucleus into the cytoplasm where it directs the synthesis of proteins. Transfer RNA is a smaller RNA molecule which is found predominately in the cytoplasm. Transfer RNA brings individual components of the protein molecule called amino acids to the protein synthesizing sites. There is one specific transfer RNA molecule for each amino acid. Each transfer RNA molecule serves as a special handle to carry the amino acid to the site of synthesis.

How does the whole protein synthesizing process take place? DNA in the nucleus directs the formation of messenger RNA.[120] The messenger RNA has a nucleotide sequence which is a complementary copy of the sequence in the DNA. Thus, the DNA molecule provides a template on whose surface the messenger RNA is formed. The messenger RNA is assembled by the attraction of individual RNA nucleotides to the DNA strand. The first step is the transfer of information from DNA to messenger RNA. The messenger RNA moves from the nucleus into the cytoplasm. In the cytoplasm, the messenger RNA unites with protein synthesizing sites. The protein synthesizing sites in the cytoplasm are called ribosomes. A ribosome is itself a globular protein which encloses a messenger RNA molecule. Transfer RNA molecules carrying amino acids are attracted to the surface of the messenger RNA molecule. As mentioned previously, there are several different kinds of transfer RNA molecules.[130] Each molecule carries a particular amino acid for which it is a specific carrier molecule. Each transfer RNA molecule has a specific sequence of nucleotides which forms the code letters identifying the kind of amino acid carried by the transfer RNA. The sequence of nucleotides forming the code letters is called an anticodon. The anticodon of the transfer RNA will attach to a specific site on the messenger RNA. The binding site on the messenger RNA is capable of forming hydrogen bonds with the anticodon. Therefore, the transfer RNA molecules, carrying amino acids, attach to the messenger RNA molecule in a predetermined sequence. The amino acids carried by the transfer RNA are therefore brought into close spatial arrangement in a sequential order determined by the messenger RNA base sequence. The amino acids are linked to each other while being held on the messenger RNA surface. As each amino acid is linked to its neighbor, the transfer RNA molecule is released. The sequence of linked amino acids forms a protein molecule. The structure of the protein molecule is its pattern of folding and spatial organization.[150] This is determined by the number and kind of amino acids contained in the protein molecule. Thus, the structure of the protein molecule is determined by the messenger RNA code. This in turn was determined by the nuclear DNA which produced it. We see, therefore, that there is a flow of information from DNA to messenger RNA to transfer RNA which determines the protein structure. Proteins are the structural units of cell oganization and also act as catalysts called enzymes which regulate chemical processes essential to maintenance of life. Indirectly, the information stored in DNA determines the destiny of the cell. Purines, pyrimidine, ribose, nucleosides, and nucleotides are the chemical alphabet in the information flow within a cell.

Analysis of Lesson One

Lesson One is intended to teach knowledge of specific facts, concepts, trends, and sequences. The major outcome objective is knowledge of nucleic acid structure and function. Little attention is given to illustrations of cognitive skills. The lesson is obviously organized as a reception task with serial-centered structure. The ideas are ordered in a linear fashion with each idea flowing into the next one with considerable amount of commonality.

The first 102 statements in the lesson are classified as belonging to cell 1 (see Chapter One). The discussion concerns a constant feature of all living cells, namely, the structure and information-carrying capacity of the nucleic acid complement of the cell. The major portion of the discussion is on nucleic acid structure as a general property of living cells. The remaining part of the lesson, from statement 103 to the end, can be classified as an example of cell 2 organization. The focus of attention moves from nucleic acid structure to its function—still, however, at a general level and as a constant feature of most living cells. The lesson, therefore, is relatively simple in its sequential organization. The lesson could have been lengthened to include a discussion of protein synthesis in specific cells such as bacteria, yeast, higher plant, and mammalian cells. If this had been done, then the lesson sequence would be classified as moving toward cell 6 which includes discussion of specific examples of processes as a constant feature of the specific instances cited. Moreover, the discussion could have been further amplified by citing conditions in a generalized model of a living cell where DNA-directed protein synthesis is a variable phenomenon. This would encourage classifying that segment of the lesson as cell 4—variable process presented as a generality.

This serial-centered lesson is hierarchically organized. Each topic in sequence is subsumed by the next one. Thus, the nitrogenous bases are subsumed within the concept of nucleoside, nucleosides are contained within the concept of nucleotides, and all of these are subsumed within the ultimate concepts of polynucleotide and double helix.

The sequential structure of the lesson will be analyzed using a Kinetogram as explained in Chapter Two. To prepare a Kinetogram, a code number is assigned to every technical word contained in each statement in the lesson. The code number is used thereafter to represent the word. (A list of coded words is presented in Appendix A. The code numbers assigned to each statement are given in Appendix B where the statement code number appears at left followed by a list of the code numbers assigned to that statement.) For example, statement number 1 is assigned code numbers 1, 2, 3, and 4 representing the technical words *living cell, assemblage, molecules,* and *functions.* Each consecu-

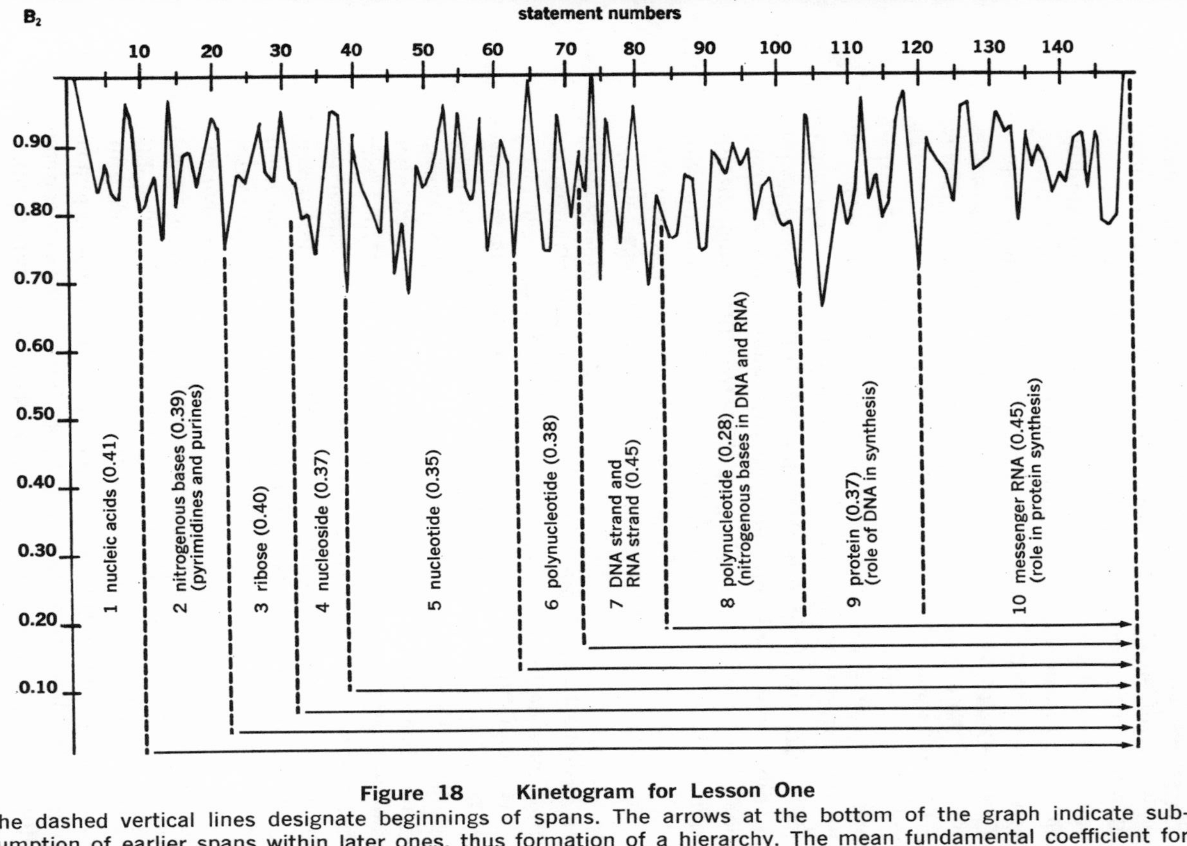

Figure 18 Kinetogram for Lesson One

The dashed vertical lines designate beginnings of spans. The arrows at the bottom of the graph indicate subsumption of earlier spans within later ones, thus formation of a hierarchy. The mean fundamental coefficient for each span is shown in parentheses.

tive pair of coded statements is analyzed to obtain a fundamental coefficient value (B_1). The average value (B_1) is obtained for the list. For Lesson One, $B_1=0.38$. This means that, on the average, over one-third of the technical terms in each pair of statements are linking terms. That is, more than one-third of the terms in each pair of statements are held in common. In addition to B_1 values, weighted coefficients (B_2) are obtained and plotted as a Kinetogram. The Kinetogram for Lesson One is presented as Figure 18. There are several characteristics of the Kinetogram which should be understood before making interpretations about the structure of a communication. Those parts of the graph that contain points near the abscissa, or form an upward-directed line, represent segments of high sequential structure (kinetic structure). Those parts of the graph that contain points clearly depressed below the abscissa represent segments of the lesson with low structure. High-structured sequences in Figure 18 occur in statements 22 through 30, 50 through 59, and 120 through 134. A clearly low-structured sequence occurs between statements 82 and 103. This part of the graph is depressed in relation to the surrounding points in the graph.

The Kinetogram (Figure 18) and code summary sheet (Appendix B) are used to identify blocks of discourse called spans. There are ten spans in the lesson. They are marked on the code summary sheet with brackets. The beginning of each span (block of ideas related to one or more highly frequent code words) is marked on the Kinetogram with vertical dashed lines. The major idea discussed in each span is identified by name following the span number. Thus span 1 consists largely of a discussion of nucleic acids. The mean fundamental coefficient for the span has been computed and reported on the Kinetogram as the numerical value in parentheses following the name of the dominant idea discussed in the span. Thus, in span 1, the B_1 is 0.41; in span 2, the B_1 is 0.39; and so forth. Usually there is a major downward-directed spike at the point where a span begins. This large amplitude spike indicates that a high frequency idea has been introduced. Moreover, the code summary sheet (Appendix B) usually shows that some word or group of words begins an intensive and extended run at that point in the list. These are the kinds of evidence used in defining the beginning point of each span. The code number of the dominant word in each span is given with the word to the right of the bracket.

The following conclusions about the structure of Lesson One can be made by analyzing the Kinetogram. Most of the spans have high sequential structure with the exception of span 8. The mean fundamental coefficient for this span is 0.28—a value lower than that of the other spans. This is a reasonable observation since the strictly serial order of the lesson is partially reduced to a cluster-centered mode in span 8. In this span the relationship of nitrogenous bases in DNA and RNA strands is being discussed. This requires a considerable amount of discussion about the spatial and functional relationships of many of the components presented earlier in the lesson. The graph is depressed at this point as one might expect when the mean fundamental coefficient is low. The high-structured spans in the lesson as observed in the Kinetogram are spans 1, 3, 7, and 10 which have B_1 values equal to or greater than 0.40. In previous analyses of biology lessons obtained in high school classrooms we have found a range of B_1 values for the total lesson of 0.24 to 0.44. The variation in mean B_1 values for Lesson One spans can be evaluated in relation to this range. Clearly, a value of 0.28 (span 8) is near the lower limit of those we have observed. The high values of 0.40 to 0.45 fall at the upper end of the previously observed range. The mean B_1 of 0.38 for the whole lesson is clearly near the upper end of the range. The lesson statements have been numbered for your convenience in correlating Kinetogram data with the lesson discourse. You will probably want to examine the lesson to determine the span origins as indicated on the Kinetogram and analyze the content of high-structured spans as opposed to low-structured ones. Finally, the hierarchical structure of the lesson is apparent in the sequential presentation of the ideas. The more elementary and fundamental concepts are presented before the next more advanced and inclusive concepts. The arrows drawn at the bottom of the Kinetogram indicate the hierarchical arrangement of the content. One can see that the content of each span is continued within and subsumed by successive spans as demonstrated by the stair-step arrangement of the arrows extending to the end of the lesson. The linear organization of the lesson is also apparent from the logical sequential arrangement of the ideas. Each component is discussed completely before moving to the next related component of the nucleic acid theme; finally, the lesson culminates with a general discussion of the process of protein synthesis. Note that the structure of the last two spans, where this topic is discussed, is rather high ($B_1 = 0.37$ and 0.45). This should be anticipated, since each step in the protein synthesis process is discussed in order of actual occurrence and is carefully related to the next step in succession.

Lesson Two Information-Carrying Molecules: The Nucleic Acids

Transmittal of information in living systems can assume many forms. At the most obvious level we know that animals communicate with one another. The songs of birds, the sounds of insects, and the languages of man are commonly experienced forms of information transmittal. There are, however, more subtle forms of communication. Some animals deposit chemical molecules that can be smelled or sensed by other animals coming along the same path. These information molecules allow communication between animals over long periods of time. The information molecules are sufficiently stable to last for long periods of time. We see that chemical molecules can transmit information in a way analogous to information transmission by sounds. The evidence for the communication is that another animal responds to the sound or to the deposited chemical in some predictable way. Likewise, within individual organisms there are chemical molecules called hormones which regulate body functions and maintain balance in activity among various organs.[10] Hormones may rightly be called information molecules since they carry messages from one part of the body to another. Even at the cellular level, we find molecules capable of storing and transmitting information. These molecules are called nucleic acids. They have the all-important function of regulating cell growth, differentiation, and metabolism. The effects of the nucleic acids in regulating cellular metabolism clearly influences the total organism since so many body functions are dependent on the activities of individual cells. In this lesson we discuss the various kinds of nucleic acids found in living cells. We compare their structures and functions in relation to their role as information molecules.

There are two major groups of nucleic acids, labelled DNA and RNA. They differ in chemical structure, cellular distribution, and function. In order to set forth the chemical differences between RNA and DNA, we need first to examine their similarities.[20] Both DNA and RNA are composed of unit molecules called nucleotides. A nucleotide is a large molecule containing a nitrogenous base, a sugar molecule, and a phosphate.

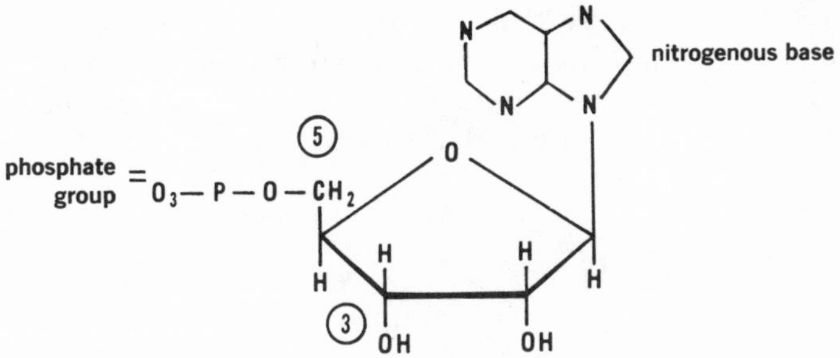

nucleotide

The nitrogenous bases are of two kinds—purines and pyrimidines. Both RNA and DNA have purine bases. Pyrimidine bases differ for DNA and RNA with the exception of one called cytosine that is common to both DNA and RNA molecules. A pyrimidine is a nitrogenous base containing carbon, nitrogen, hydrogen, and oxygen atoms which form a hexagonal ring structure. There are two nitrogen atoms in the pyrimidine ring.

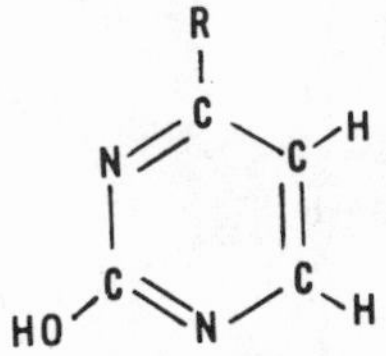

pyrimidine

The atoms attached to the carbon atoms in the ring determine the specific kind of pyrimidine. Purines contain two rings, one being a pyrimidine.

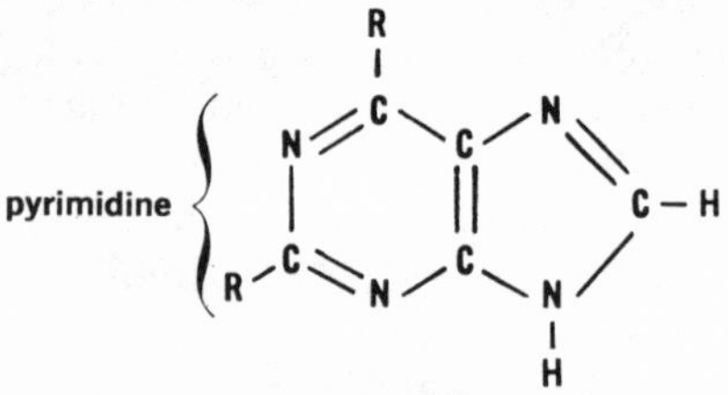

pyrimidine

purine

The other ring, containing five atoms, is fused with the pyrimidine ring.[30] There are three kinds of pyrimidine bases: cytosine, uracil, and thymine. The cytosine base has a nitrogen and oxygen bonded to the ring. The uracil base has only oxygen groups, and the thymine base has oxygen and a carbon atom.

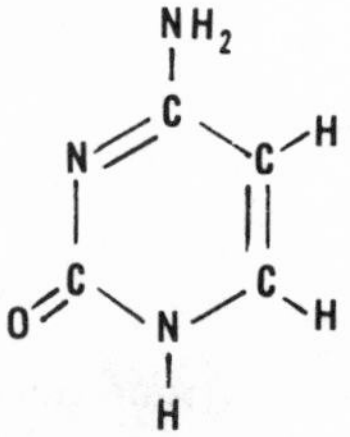

cytosine

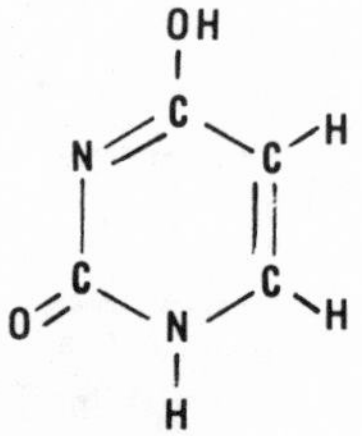

uracil

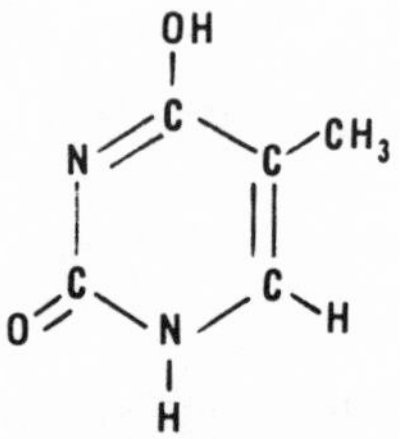

thymine

There are two kinds of purines: adenine and guanine. Adenine contains a sole nitrogen-containing group bonded to the ring, whereas guanine contains a nitrogen and an oxygen atom bonded to the ring.

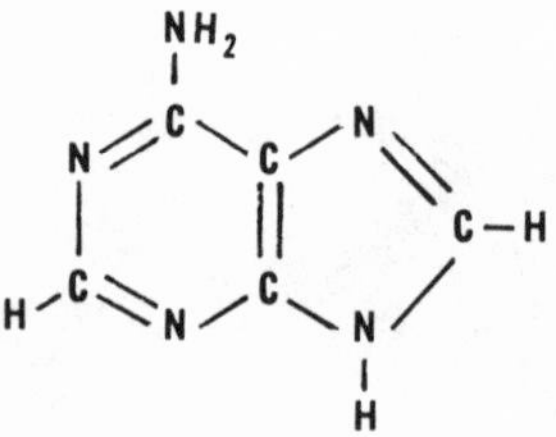

adenine

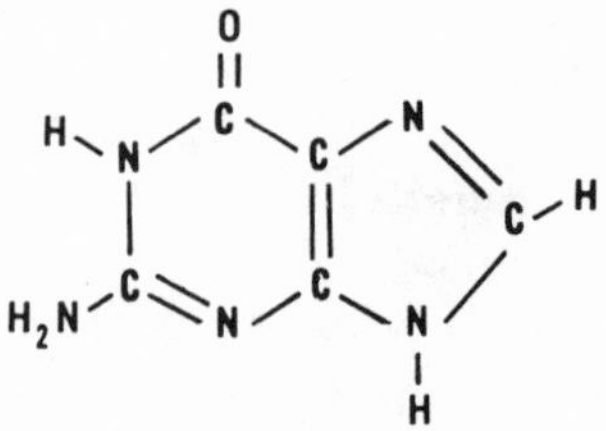

guanine

DNA molecules and RNA molecules both contain adenine, guanine, and cytosine bases. RNA molecules contain uracil. DNA molecules contain thymine.

RNA bases	*DNA bases*
adenine	adenine
guanine	guanine
cytosine	cytosine
uracil	thymine

In addition to having different base composition, DNA and RNA also have different kinds of sugar molecules. RNA contains a ribose molecule.[40] This sugar molecule has an oxygen on both the second and third carbon atoms in the ring.

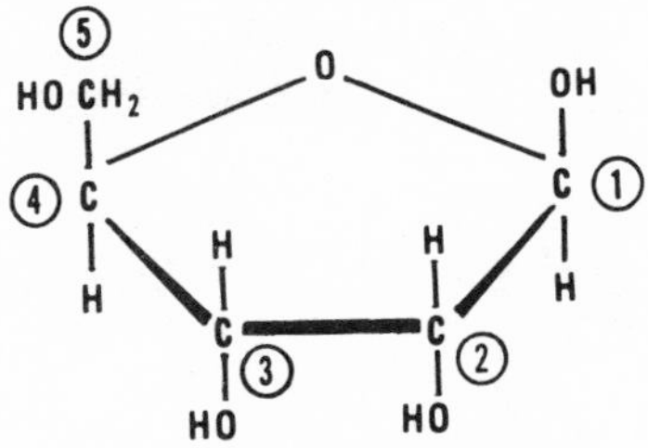

ribose

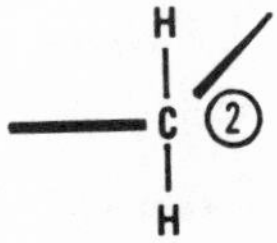

deoxyribose

DNA contains a sugar molecule with one less oxygen. It is called deoxyribose. The term deoxyribose describes a ribose molecule that has lost one oxygen atom.

When a nitrogenous base bonds to the first carbon of either kind of ribose molecule, the resulting combination is called a nucleoside. There are RNA nucleosides and DNA nucleosides. The characteristics distinguishing the two are the kind of ribose sugar molecule and sometimes the kind of pyrimidine base as explained earlier.

The addition of a phosphate to a nucleoside produces a nucleotide. The phosphate is linked to the fifth carbon atom of the ribose to form a phospho-ester linkage. An ester linkage is the product of the union of an acid and an alcohol.[50] The phosphate acts as an acid and the fifth carbon atom contains an alcohol group. The linkage between the two is known as a phosphoester linkage since a phosphate molecule is involved. Both DNA and RNA nucleotides form long chain molecules called polynucleotides. A polynucleotide is a chain of nucleotides. There may be several hundred or more nucleotides in a single polynucleotide. The term polynucleotide uses the Greek prefix *poly* meaning many. Thus, a polynucleotide is a long chain of many linked nucleotides. Any two nucleotides in the whole sequence are called a dinucleotide.

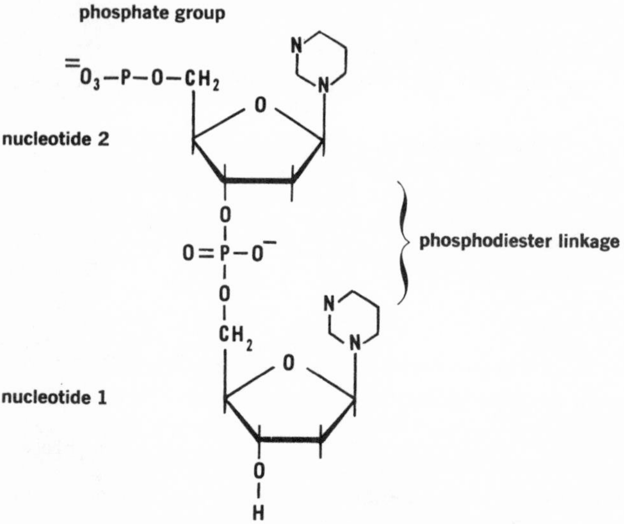

phosphate group

$^{=}O_3{-}P{-}O{-}CH_2$

nucleotide 2

phosphodiester linkage

nucleotide 1

The nucleotides are joined by a phosphodiester linkage extending from the fifth carbon of one ribose molecule to the third carbon of the next. The polynucleotide strands consist of a phosphate and sugar backbone with free nitrogenous bases projecting outward.[60] The presence of free purines and pyrimidines projecting into space favors cross linking of pairs of polynucleotide strands. The two strands are linked by bonds called hydrogen bonds. A hydrogen bond is a chemical linkage between an oxygen and a hydrogen atom. The oxygen and hydrogen atoms must be spatially proximate to favor stable bond formation. In DNA polynucleotides, an adenine group hydrogen bonds with a thymine, and a guanine group hydrogen bonds with a cytosine. The specific pairs of bases are cross linked since their arrangement of oxygen

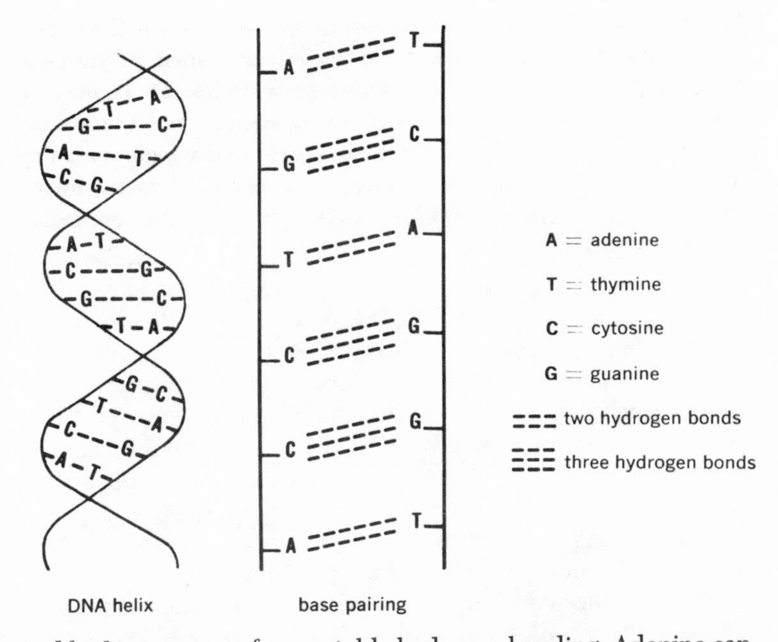

and hydrogen atoms favors stable hydrogen bonding. Adenine can pair with thymine since two hydrogen bonds are formed between them. Guanine can pair with cytosine since three hydrogen bonds can be formed between them. All other combinations do not allow stable hydrogen bonding. In DNA, the cross linked double strands form the well-known double helix.[70] In RNA, there is similar base pairing based on the same principle of hydrogen bonding. Adenine pairs with uracil and, again, guanine pairs with cytosine. There is information in the base sequence in the RNA and DNA strands. We can consider each base as a letter of a code word. Then suppose three bases (three letters) taken together in sequence form a code word. This is very similar to Morse telegraph code in which certain combinations of dots and dashes form words. We can conclude that RNA and DNA molecules are rich in potential stores of information since many words can be represented by the long polynucleotide sequences of base triplets.

DNA and RNA differ in cellular distribution. DNA is found mostly in the nucleus. RNA occurs predominately in the cytoplasm.[80] There is some DNA in mitochondria and chloroplasts of cells. Mitochondrial DNA, however, is much smaller than the polynucleotides in the nucleus. There are differences in the function of DNA and RNA. DNA is a source of stored information about regulating cell structure and function. DNA regulates changes in cell activity by influencing protein production. Proteins are the building blocks of cell structure and the molecules that directly regulate metabolic activity.

RNA occurs as two kinds—messenger RNA and transfer RNA. Messenger RNA is produced by DNA in the nucleus and migrates into the cytoplasm. The messenger RNA serves as a code to direct protein synthesis. Transfer RNA is a smaller molecule than messenger RNA.[90] Its function is to transfer protein subunits called amino acids to the sites of protein synthesis. There is a specific transfer RNA for each amino acid. We may think of the transfer RNA as a kind of handle for carrying amino acids to the protein synthesizing sites. The messenger RNA, however, is an information carrying molecule. It carries the message from DNA to the protein synthesizing sites. Transfer RNA is a kind of shuttle molecule carrying amino acids to the messenger RNA where protein synthesis will occur. Each transfer RNA molecule will bind to a certain site on the messenger RNA called a codon. This site is the location of a base sequence triplet which pairs with the transfer RNA triplet called an anticodon. Therefore, the messenger RNA influences the sequence in which transfer RNA molecules bind to its surface. This in turn controls the sequence of amino acids linked to form a protein molecule.[100] The complete translation of DNA-stored information occurs when the protein molecule is synthesized on the messenger RNA strand. DNA controls messenger RNA structure. Messenger RNA structure controls the sequential binding of transfer RNA to its surface. Since each transfer RNA molecule carries a specific amino acid molecule, the sequential order of protein structure is determined. Protein molecules serve two major functions in the cell: (1) they are the structural units of cell organization, and (2) they are catalysts regulating metabolic processes in the cell. There is a definite division of function between nucleic acids and proteins in cell function. Nucleic acids are information storage and transfer molecules. Proteins are structural and chemical catalytic molecules.[110] Among the nucleic acids, DNA is an information storage molecule. RNA is an information carrier molecule which aids translation of the information into its terminal expression as a protein molecule.

Analysis of Lesson Two

This lesson is also on the topic of nucleic acids as information-carrying molecules. However, the organization here is clearly different from that of Lesson One. The outcome objective is the same as that for the first lesson—communication of knowledge of nucleic acid structure and function. This lesson is organized as a reception task with a cluster-centered structure. The sequential organization of this lesson is less linear than that of Lesson One. Moreover, ideas are continuously being placed in juxtaposition by comparisons and contrasts, and by citing relationships to concepts and principles which subsume the specifics as clusters of content throughout the lesson. The sequential build-up of this lesson is more complex than of the first lesson when analyzed according to the eight cell model. Statements 1 through 18 are classified as belonging to cell 2. The process of information flow is discussed at a general level and as a constant phenomenon among many kinds of organisms and at various levels of biological organization. This should be contrasted with Lesson One which began with content classified as belonging to cell 1. It is obvious that Lesson Two begins with a completely different thrust than the preceding lesson. Statements 19 through 82 contain content classified as belonging to cell 1 in the eight cell model. The final part of the lesson, statements 83 to the end, can be classified as examples of cell 2. Thus the lesson contains three steps as classified according to the eight cell model; namely, cell 2 to cell 1 to cell 2. The lesson begins and ends with the same organizational pattern although the content differs. The first part of the lesson concerns the concept of information flow whereas the last part of the lesson concerns protein biosynthesis.

The sequential structure of Lesson Two is analyzed, as it was for Lesson One, using a Kinetogram (Figure 19). The mean fundamental coefficient for the total lesson is $B_1 = 0.31$. There are ten

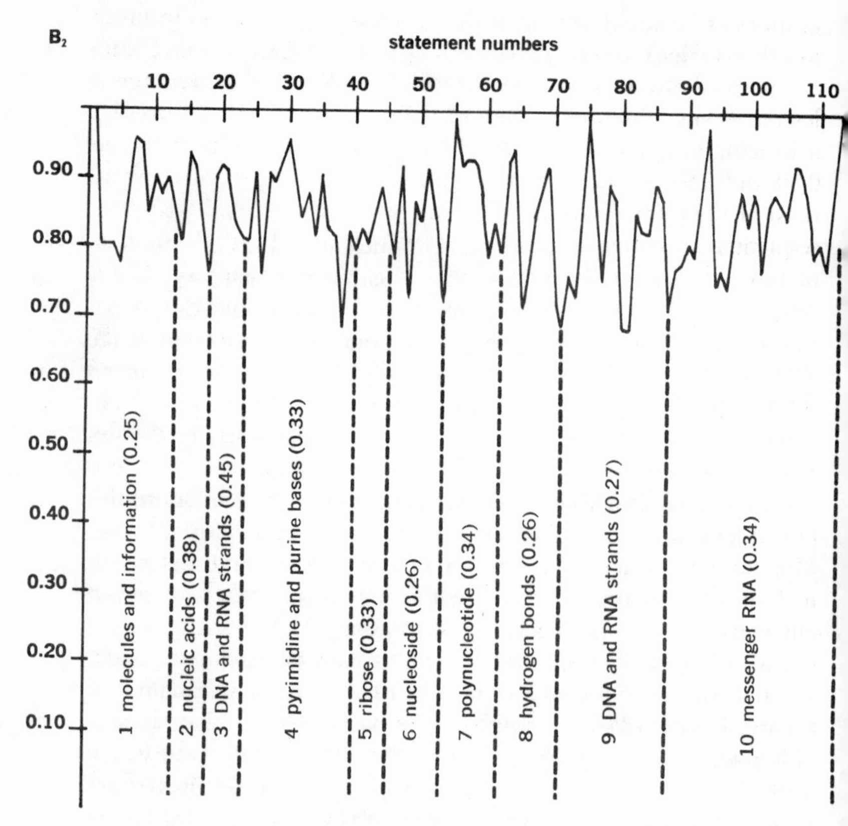

Figure 19 Kinetogram for Lesson Two
The organization of this graph is the same as that of Figure 18.

spans in the lesson. The range of mean fundamental coefficients is 0.25 to 0.45. Clearly, the B_1 of 0.45 for span 3 on the topic of DNA and RNA strands is an exceptional instance in this lesson. The majority of the spans have mean B_1 values less than 0.35. The mean B_1 of 0.31 for the whole lesson is expected for a cluster-centered lesson. In general, the graph is composed of points somewhat depressed below the abscissa. At places, there are brief sequences of high structure, as for example in statements 54 through 58. This sequence appears in the middle of the Kinetogram as an elevated section of the graph in span 7. In comparison to other biology lessons, analyzed with Kinetograms, this lesson is intermediate in structure. It clearly is not a low-structured lesson. A low-structured lesson of the same length would present a Kinetogram with most of the points falling in a range between 0.50 and 0.85 on the B_2 axis (left-hand ordinate). In this lesson, most of the plotted points fall within a range of 0.70 to 0.95. The sequential development of the lesson is shown by the sequence of topics listed for the secondary spans. Some of the topics are repeated in the course of the lesson. DNA and RNA strands are discussed in spans 3 and 9. An examination of the code summary sheet in Appendix C shows that many code words are interspersed throughout the statements and that many of the spans contain a more heterogeneous collection of code numbers than did the spans in Lesson One.

In general, the Kinetogram for Lesson One has a greater number of upward-directed points forming peaks near the abscissa. Moreover, the trace is generally more elevated in Figure 18 than in Figure 19. It is clear that most of the mean fundamental coefficients for the spans in Lesson One are higher than for the spans in Lesson Two. The first lesson is hierarchically organized, whereas the second lesson is not. In relation to general learning theory, Lesson One was organized in small steps with considerable reinforcement of ideas in moving from one statement to the next. This is consistent with Skinner's concept of immediate reinforcement and sequential ordering of tasks to maximize chaining of responses. This is also consistent with the biopsychological model of communication presented in Chapter Two which predicts that knowledge acquisition is enhanced when content is ordered sequentially such that consecutive statements contain commonality (linkage of ideas from one statement to the next). The hierarchical organization of Lesson One should enhance the orderliness and stability of acquired knowledge. Both Ausubel and Gagné recognize the value of hierarchical lesson sequences in facilitating knowledge acquisition and increasing its cognitive stability. The second lesson is organized around general biological principles consistent with Bruner's concept of subject matter structure wherein specific facts are embedded within an over-arching idea that integrates and interrelates the content. This is a cluster-centered lesson and has less serial structure than the first one, but more multiple relationships among diverse ideas. The use of comparisons and contrasts, when discussing the various kinds of nucleic acids, is intended to enhance acquisition of clearly differentiated concepts. The attributes of DNA, messenger RNA, and transfer RNA are concisely set forth and the differences in attributes among the three are cited. Comparisons are made directly among the various kinds of nucleic acids rather than setting forth each one independently. Although the content may be somewhat more difficult to follow than in the first lesson, it is presented at a higher level of abstraction and should facilitate the formation of a general understanding of the structure and role of nucleic acids as information carrying molecules.

The reader may find a clearly different emotional response in reading Lesson Two in comparison to Lesson One. The highly structured, linear ordering of Lesson One may be too confining for the mature reader who knows something about the field. Lesson Two is less linear, incorporates more diversity in the content presented, and therefore may be more appealing. The highly structured lesson is easier to follow, but is much more compulsively ordered than the cluster-centered lesson. There is evidence to show, however, that naive students acquire greater stores of specific knowledge with the organization used in Lesson One. Therefore, the wise teacher plans to present a highly structured lesson to maximize pupil knowledge acqiusition and then follow that with a cluster-centered lesson to develop cognitive flexibility in using the knowledge.

Lesson Three Cell Membrane Structure and Function: A Search for Accurate Models

One of the most fascinating fields of modern biological research is the study of cell membrane structure and function. For some time, biologists questioned whether a clearly organized boundary existed at a cell surface. They wondered whether the surface of the cell represented a mere temporary collection of molecules, forming a thin surface film, or whether there was indeed a physically stable envelope surrounding the cell. The light microscope is not sensitive enough to allow observations of cell surface fine structure. With the electron microscope, however, the surface of the cell can be examined in fine detail. Very thin sections of fixed cells and fractured surfaces of frozen cells clearly show the presence of an identifiable multi-layered membrane. The consistent appearance of a multi-layered envelope in numerous cells suggests that an external limiting membrane is a constant structural feature of most living cells. The evidence in support of this conclusion must be weighed in the light of artifacts produced in the preparation of tissues for electron microscopy. Chemical fixatives are usually employed and these may alter the molecular structure of tissue. Indeed, the observed multi-layered membrane could be a damage artifact of fixation. However, this seems less than likely since frozen fractured cells, which are not treated with chemicals, clearly show on their cell surfaces a layered membrane structure. Since rapidly frozen cells are not likely to undergo gross chemical alteration during freezing, it is not expected that the observed membrane structure is a chemical artifact. Some researchers argue that any change that results in altered metabolism and eventual cell death can bring about abnormal cell structure. The membrane observed in the electron microscope may be only a denatured assembly of molecules not normally distributed as a continuous sheet at the cell surface. Evidence contrary to this view is that red blood cells can be lysed to yield a clearly isolatable cell membrane called a red blood cell ghost. The integrity of that ghost after repeated washing and centrifugation clearly substantiates the reality of a red blood cell membrane. Although most biologists agree that cell membranes are identifiable, relatively stable surface structures, there is considerable debate about the molecular organization of the cell membrane. Electron microscopic examination of thin cell sections have shown that the internal volume of a cell is richly supplied with membrane networks. Most cellular organelles are membrane-bound. In some cases it looks as though these membranes are of a different structure than the outer cell membrane. The prospects for clearly indentifying a single model of cell membrane structure suitable for all types of external and internal membrane appear unencouraging.

The task of explaining cell membrane function is equally filled with uncertainties. There is no question that the external cell membrane performs a remarkable range of functions in regulating material passage between the cell interior and the environment. It is also a surface containing many enzymes essential for metabolic activity of the cell. Indeed, there is increasing evidence that many of the selective transport activities of the membrane may depend on metabolic energy. Inner cell membranes, especially those surrounding cellular organelles, may regulate material transport between the organelle and the cytoplasm wherein they are embedded. The external cell membrane of many kinds of cells not only demonstrates selective regulation of ion uptake but may literally pump ions from inside the cell to the exterior even when there is a greater ion concentration on the outside than on the inside. Given the apparently enormous complexity and diversity of functions of cell membrane, it is not surprising that the search for a reasonably accurate model of the cell surface continues to be a pressing problem of biological research. We survey now some of the current competing models of cell membrane structure, and then turn our attention to models of cell membrane function.

The Danielli-Davson Model. One of the earliest and most widely accepted models of cell membrane structure is that of J. F. Danielli and H. Davson who proposed a laminated membrane structure in 1935, long before electron microscope evidence was available to support it. In their model, the membrane is a lipo-protein complex consisting of a lipid bilayer covered on its two outer surfaces with a layer of protein. The lipid molecules are oriented with their polar groups in contact with the protein layer and their fatty acyl tails in opposition to one another. Danielli and Davson assumed that the polar (charged) groups of the lipid molecules would form polar linkages with charged groups on the protein. Likewise, the fatty acyl chains could form stable associations by hydrophobic bonding to one another.

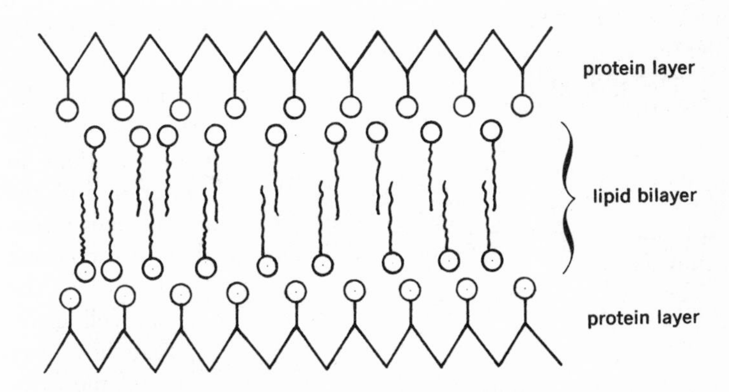

Cross-Section View of A Bilayer Membrane

What evidence could be used to support the bilayer model of Danielli and Davson? In 1925, a full decade earlier, Gorter and Grendel had published an interesting finding that red blood cell membrane lipid when deposited on a water surface spread to form a monolayer with an area twice that of the surface of the red blood cell. Their data suggested that the lipid must be packed within the membrane in such a way that the surface area covered by the lipid was reduced to one-half its total possible area. The Danielli-Davson model satisfied this requirement by stacking the lipid molecules in a bilayer; the molecules thus occupied only one-half the total area required if they were distributed in a monolayer. Although Gorter and Grendel's data have been widely accepted, there is some question about whether the area occupied by the lipid extracted from a cell membrane was accurately computed. Thus, we cannot rely completely on their data to support the Danielli-Davson model. Indirect evidence in support of the model comes from observations on physical properties of cell membranes. The sea urchin egg, stripped of its external coats, is sufficiently large to allow careful observation of its surface physical properties. When electrodes are properly placed within the egg and upon its surface, one can measure the electrical resistance of the membrane. The electrical resistance is sufficiently high to suggest that the membrane contains a rich concentration of nonpolar molecules within it. This would suggest a lipid layer as proposed in the Danielli-Davson model. Further evidence in support of this point is that when an oil droplet is placed on the surface of an egg membrane, it rapidly penetrates the membrane indicating the presence of a fatty substance in the membrane. The change in surface tension (its resistance to deformation) of the membrane clearly supports the view that some component of the membrane in addition to lipid produces a reduction in surface tension. Proteins are a logical choice because of their abundance in cells and their surface-active properties. Proteins are long polymers capable of forming sheets by lateral cohesion. This property also supports the Danielli-Davson model. One should be aware, however, that protein polymers also form globules. The sheet structure is only one of several possible forms of protein structure. The foregoing electron microscopic and physical evidence support the general properties of the Danielli-Davson model. Much of the evidence is indirect and therefore is not as strong as one would like to have.

Now we need to discuss diffusion across the bilayer membrane. If the basic architecture of the cell membrane is sandwich-like, with oily substances in the middle, and polar (water attracting) protein sheets on the outside, what implications for membrane function can be deduecd? That is, given the properties stated by Danielli and Davson, what extrapolations can we make to predict membrane regulation of diffusion across its boundaries. According to Danielli, there are three possible barriers to diffusion across a cell membrane: (1) the membrane/water interface for diffusion into the membrane; (2) the membrane/water interface for diffusion from the membrane into a water filled space; and (3) diffusion across the interior of the membrane. Molecules with many hydroxyl groups form close linkages with water. They do not enter the membrane very easily. Therefore, for them, barrier (1) is the most critical. These molecules, (sugars and glycerol, for example) move very slowly across the membrane. Molecules with largely non-polar groups (oily substances) penetrate the membrane rapidly, but are not rapidly passed into the cell. They are retarded in the lipid layer by linkage with other oily substances in the lipid layer. Molecules having many polar and non-polar groups penetrate slowly since both barriers (1) and (2) are important. The molecule cannot easily separate from the water phase since it forms linkages with the hydrogens of water molecules. The molecules are also retarded in moving from the membrane into the cell interior since the non-polar groups form hydrophobic bonds with the membrane lipids. Molecules with few polar and few non-polar groups penetrate comparatively rapidly. They form few retarding bonds with either the water or lipid layers. Based on these predictions, we can list compounds in decreasing order of permeability rate. The molecules at the top of the list penetrate most rapidly while those at the bottom penetrate most slowly.

1. Oxygen and methyl alcohol
2. Glycerols, sugar, and glycogen
3. Carotene, vitamin A, and large fat molecules
4. Polyhydroxylic bile acids and proteins

Danielli subsequently realized that his membrane model would have to be modified to better explain the rapid penetration of water and solutes. If the membrane contained a continuous lipid layer, the permeability to water and solutes would be too low. He therefore proposed a model with channels running through the membrane. Each channel was lined with protein molecules whose polar groups provided a water filled passage for rapid diffusion of polar substances and ions.

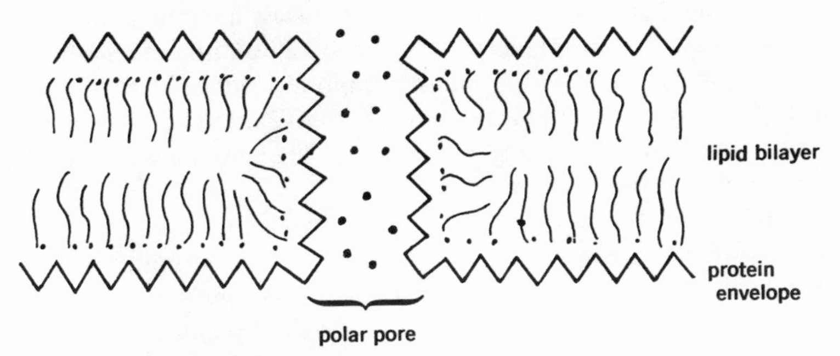

Cross-Section of the Danielli-Davson Membrane

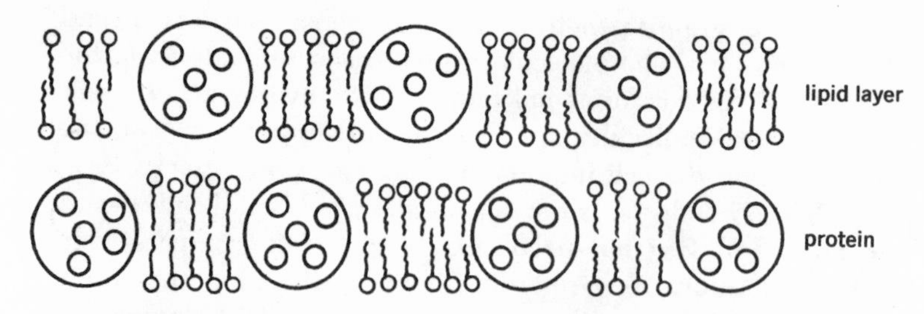

Cross-Section of a Globular Lipid and Protein Membrane Model

For at least three decades, the bilayer membrane model or modifications thereof have been accepted widely in the academic community. Modifications were often small. Globular proteins were added to the surface of the membrane and, in some cases, the sheet-like protein was removed and only globular proteins were placed on the lipid surface. In other modifications, globular and cable protein were interspersed with lipid globules to form a patchwork organization.

Mosaic Membrane Models. This transition toward a patchwork of lipo-protein aggregates has been extended by D. F. H. Wallach. He has proposed a mosaic membrane model clearly different from the previous bilayer models. His model is built on the assumptions that (1) the protein portion of the membrane is largely globular (there are few or no sheetlike proteins), and (2) the lipid molecules are attached to the globular proteins by hydrophobic linkages, not by polar bonds as assumed in Danielli's model. According to Wallach, the most logical arrangement of lipids based on these assumptions is a mosaic pattern. Tetrads of globular proteins alternate with patches of lipid. The fatty tails of the lipid molecules form hydrophobic linkages with the non-polar surfaces of the protein.

Unit structure consists of four groups of protein globules surrounding a lipid patch. The polar groups of the lipid project into a central space producing an aqueous pore. The external surfaces of each protein tetrad must be hydrophobic to form attractive associations with the tails of lipid molecules. The inner faces of the four protein molecules can be polar, thereby stabiliz-

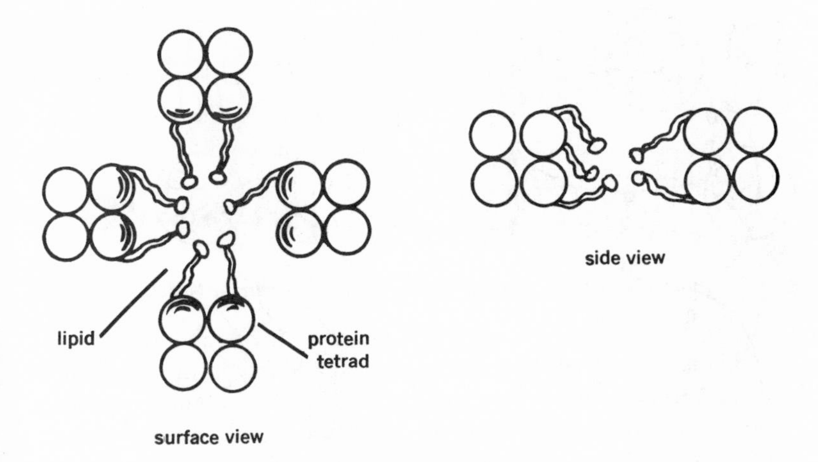

Segment of Mosaic Membrane

ing the protein-protein interaction. What is the evidence in support of Wallach's assumptions? Chemical spectroscopic analyses of membrane proteins show that most of the protein is globular. The wavelength of infra-red light absorbed by the membrane proteins suggests that most of them are helical in form and not sheet-like. The hydrogen bonds formed between oxygen and hydrogen, cross linking segments of protein chains, absorb infrared light at different wave lengths in sheet form than do helical-form proteins. Some weaker evidence in support of hydrophobic surface of protein tetrads is that hemoglobin, a naturally occurring blood protein, is arranged in globular tetrads and has sufficient non-polar protein components to form a hydrophobic (oily) surface to which fatty compounds can attach. Finally, what evidence suggests that the lipid molecules are attached to the protein by their fatty tails rather than by their charged polar groups? Nuclear magnetic resonance spectra show that the hydrogen atoms in the fatty tail are hindered much more than those in the polar head groups. This supports Wallach's assumption that the lipid molecules are attached to the the protein by their tails and not by their polar head groups. If they were attached by their polar head groups, we would find the head group hydrogen atoms to be hindered (bound to or closely packed with other atoms).

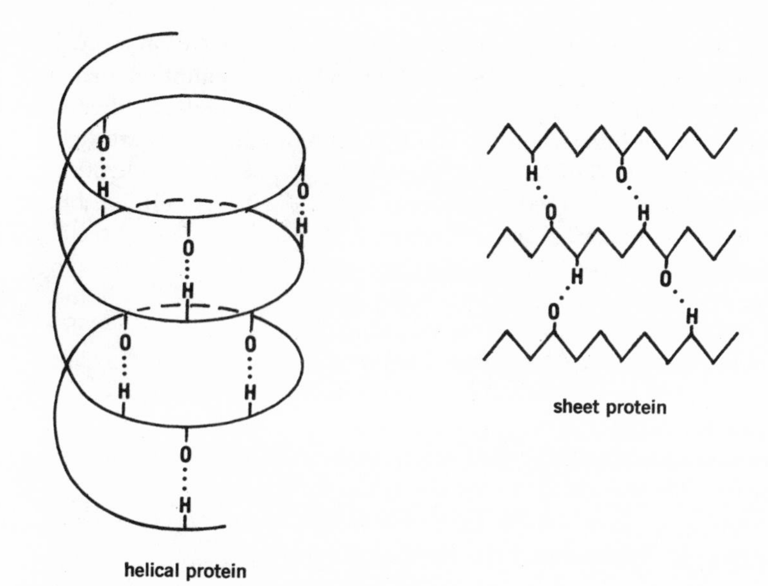

This evidence is not conclusive but is at least as strong as the evidence cited to support Danielli's membrane model.

Other mosaic models of the membrane are built on the assumption that the protein forms cuboidal subunits which are held together by lipid molecules lining their adjoining surfaces. In simple terms, we can imagine the membrane to be composed of protein bricks cemented together with lipid molecules. The lipid fatty tail is believed to be inserted between the protein subunits with the lipid polar head group projecting into the surrounding space.

There is some evidence to suggest that mitochondrial membranes and perhaps the external cell membrane are organized in

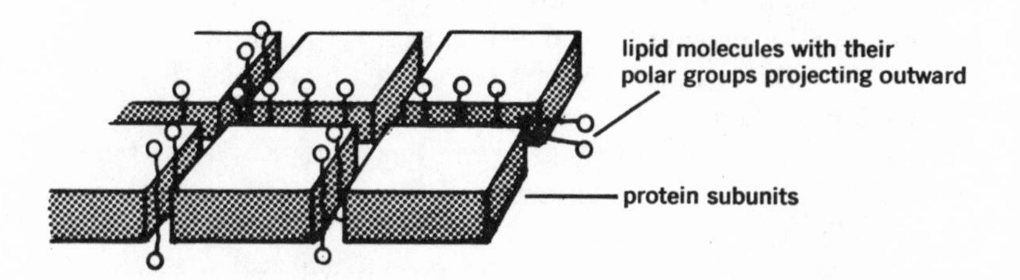

this way. Other mosaic models have been constructed on a much more random design. They are built on the assumption that a variety of lipid and protein aggregates are heaped together to form a sheet-like structure. The lipo-protein aggregates are held in a stable configuration by short-range forces (weak chemical bonds). The evidence in support of this model is not strong, but is based on empirical data. Electron microscopic images of membrane edges at high magnifications show evidence of globular aggregates closely packed within the inner layer of the membrane.

It is rather clear that the many models presented here differ substantially in structure and that the evidence in support of any one model, in preference over the remainder, is far from conclusive. Moreover, during the two decades following 1950, we have seen dramatically new interpretations of membrane organization. These radical departures from the long accepted bilayer model may have arisen from the shortcomings of the bilayer model in explaining cell membrane structure and function.

Kavanau Membrane Model. An elegant and remarkably dynamic model of the cell membrane has been proposed by J. L. Kavanau. His model is built on the assumption that the protein layer is a continuous sheet on each side of an inner lipid layer. The lipid layer, however, is presumed to be a collection of lipid globules capable of undergoing reversible transformations from a tall

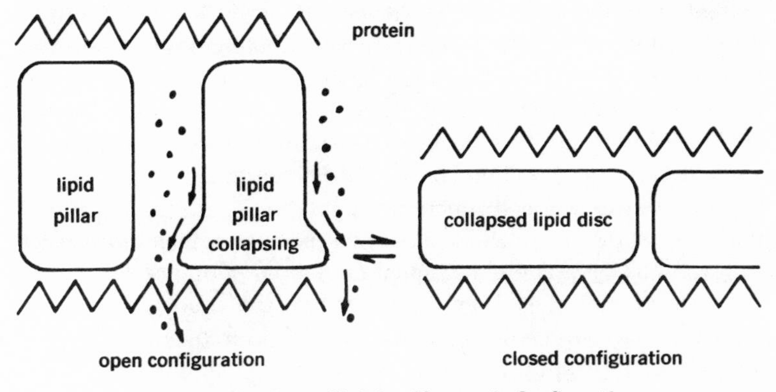

Kavanau Membrane Model — Changes in Configuration

pillar-like component (a cylinder whose axis perpendicular to the protein layer is longer than its diameter) to a disc-shaped component (whose diameter is greater than its height). When the lipid globules form pillars, there is an aqueous channel between the lipid globules allowing free passage of solutes and water across the membrane. The membrane is said to be in an open configuration. On the other hand, when the lipids form collapsed discs, the aqueous channels are obliterated and the margins of the flattened lipid discs are in contact. The membrane is said then to be in a closed configuration. Little passage of material can occur across the membrane when it is in a closed configuration.

Now, what are the mechanisms of membrane transformation? How does the open configuration become transformed to a closed configuration? Kavanau proposes that the transformation of the membrane lipid is driven by changes in hydrogen ion concentration resulting from metabolic activity. ATPase activity (enzyme cleavage of ATP into ADP plus phosphate) releases hydrogen ions. These diffuse into the protein layer where they displace calcium ions or other cations from binding sites. The calcium ions diffuse upward into the lipid layer through the aqueous channels. The calcium binds to the lipid molecules, making them less repulsed. The pillar no longer can maintain its tall cylindrical shape since the surface viscosity has been reduced. Consequently, the pillar flows downward to form a collapsed disc, thereby closing the membrane. The reverse process is achieved by calcium uptake during mitochondrial regeneration of ATP. Some free energy (energy capable of doing work) is available to begin the reverse process. As the calcium ions or other divalent cations are released from the lipid sites, smaller monovalent cations (for example Na^+) take their places. The membrane assumes an open configuration once again. The model has certain valuable qualities for interpreting cell function. Regulation of membrane transport of materials can be explained as a product of membrane lipid transformations. When the membrane lipid globules are open, diffusion of materials is enhanced. When the lipid globules are collapsed, membrane diffusion is inhibited. Moreover, by a clever application of propulsion theory, Kavanau is able to explain cellular cyclosis in terms of membrane transformations. He assumes that closure of the membrane lipid globules produces a pumping action which displaces fluids from the membrane. The flow of fluid, essentially from one side, causes a propulsion effect which pushes the membranous element in the direction opposite the flow. The assumption that membrane closure and pumping activity are directly related to cellular metabolism is reasonable. Elodea leaf cells stream most actively when they are metabolically active. Thus, by repeated opening and closing of membrane segments, various membranous organelles within the cell could be propelled through the cytoplasm. Chloroplast streaming in elodea could be the product of the membrane propulsion effect. Kavanau's explanation of membrane structure and function is supported by a collection of diverse physical chemical observations on lipid systems. The significant organizational features of the membrane model have not been verified by observation. The strength of the theory lies partly in its remarkable internal consistency. However, one must remember that impressive explanations are not worthwhile as scientific models unless they also accurately represent the events they are supposed to explain. In this respect Kavanau's model is as vulnerable as the earlier ones.

We now turn our attention to some of the unsolved problems of cell membrane function. It has been known for some time that cell membranes are selectively permeable to molecules and ions. The process of selective uptake of molecules and the regulation of uptake rate is not fully understood. There are several ways whereby molecules can penetrate cell membranes. Molecules may pass across the membrane by diffusion from a region of higher concentration to one of lower concentration. The membrane serves as an impassive barrier and does not interact directly with the diffusing material. There are two main types of transport across membranes which involve interaction of membrane components with the transported molecules: (1) facilitated diffusion, and (2) active transport. In facilitated diffusion, the cell does not expend energy in moving a molecule across the membrane. The molecule moves with a concentration gradient and the membrane merely facilitates the movement of the molecule by providing a carrier. In active transport, the cell expends energy to move molecules across the cell membrane (sometimes against a concentration gradient) from a region of lesser concentration to one of higher concentration. Again, the membrane probably has a carrier component which picks up the molecule and passes it to the other side. Energy is required to drive the mechanism, energy produced by metabolic activity of the cell.

Red Blood Cell Membrane Transport. We discuss glucose transport across red blood cell membranes as an illustration of the kinds of problems encountered in this field of inquiry. Glucose accumulation rate in red blood cells is proportional to the external concentration, increasing with external concentration until a point is reached at which further concentration increments result in no further gain in uptake rate. This negatively accelerated relationship between external glucose concentration and rate of uptake suggests that there are a finite number of carrier sites in the cell membrane. Increasing the external concentration of glucose produces an increase in glucose transport rate until most or all of the carriers become saturated and then no further increment in transport rate can be expected.

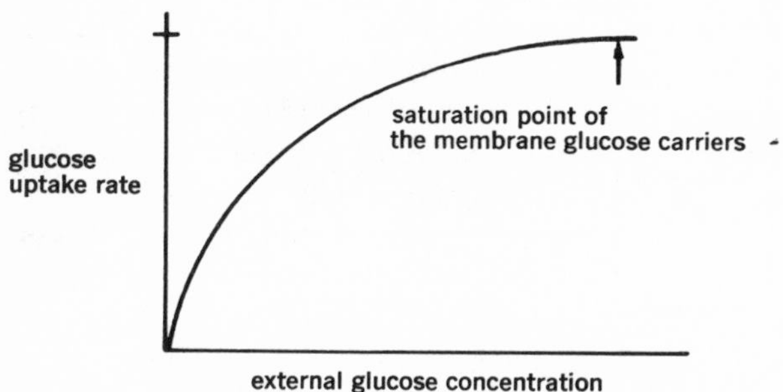

A similar relationship exists between enzyme activity and substrate concentration. This evidence suggests that the membrane carrier molecule may be a protein with a binding site analogous to the binding site of enzymes. There are at least two mechanisms that could account for the relationship between glucose uptake rate and external concentration. The simplest one is that the carriers are simple pores in the membrane. One can assume that there are a finite number of pores and hence rate of glucose uptake is proportional to the glucose concentration until all the pores become saturated. Then, no further increase in uptake rate is expected with increases in glucose concentration.

A competing explanation is that the carrier is a reorienting pore—in simple terms a revolving door mechanism which can pick up glucose only on one surface at a time. Once the glucose molecule is picked up, the carrier rotates toward the other surface of the membrane and releases the glucose. The attachment of glucose to the reorienting pore triggers its rotation to the opposite side of the membrane. However, one can assume that the rotating carrier can also revert back to the other position under random energy influences. That is, a small but significant fraction of the carrier sites can reorient spontaneously, thus opening the pore on the receiving side.

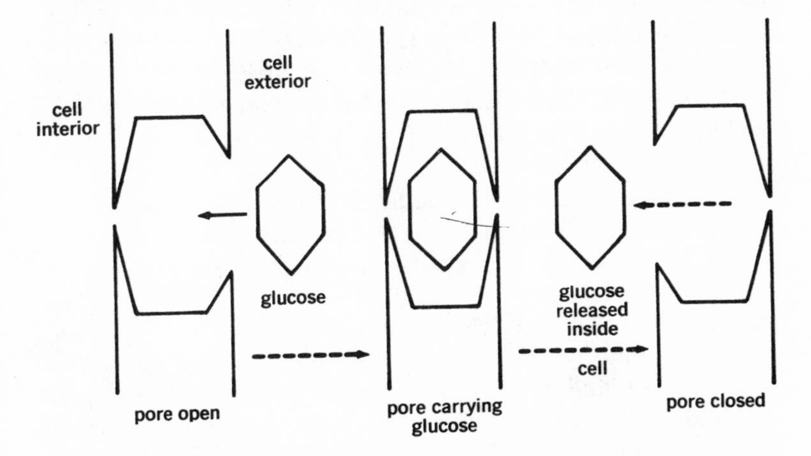

Since the presence of glucose in the reorienting pore triggers its rotation to the opposite side of the membrane, and since the pore gradually reorients toward the other side, glucose transport tends to move from the side of higher glucose concentration toward the opposite side of the membrane. An experiment is required to decide which of the models best explains glucose uptake—the simple pore (hole) model or the reorienting pore (gate) model. An analysis of the action of each model suggests the following deductions. If the simple pore model is correct, then the concentration of glucose on the inside of the red blood cell should be inversely related to the rate of uptake. A large concentration of internal glucose would cause reverse diffusion. The pores would be blocked to incoming glucose molecules by those diffusing outward. Therefore, high internal glucose concentrations should proportionately reduce the rate of external glucose uptake.

However, if the reorienting pore model is correct, then high internal glucose concentrations should facilitate glucose uptake from the external environment. The *net* gain however may be small depending on the differences in concentration between the two sides. The rationale for this prediction is that in the reorienting pore model the rate of reorientation is enhanced when glucose molecules are bound to the reorienting pore site, and thus, if there is a large internal concentration of glucose, the pores are triggered to reorient toward the external surface of the membrane where they can pick up external glucose molecules and release them on the inside. Now, each model predicts effects exactly opposite to the other, so it should be possible to test which model is accurate by observing which effect is produced in a red blood cell preparation.

One way of testing the validity of the models is to saturate red blood cells with isotope-labeled glucose. This is done by suspending the cells in radioactive-labeled glucose. The saturated cells can be collected by centrifugation and washed free of external-labeled glucose. The cells saturated with labeled glucose are divided into two equal volume samples. One sample is suspended in a saline solution containing unlabeled glucose (condition 1), the other sample is suspended in a saline solution without glucose (condition 2). If the rate of labeled glucose lose from the cells in condition 1 is greater than that in condition 2, then the reorienting pore model is correct. This would confirm that the external glucose concentration is facilitating exchange of glucose across the membrane as measured by the release of labeled glucose from the inside. On the other hand, if the loss of labeled glucose was greater in condition 2 than in condition 1, then support is gained for the simple pore model. There is less competition for the pore sites in condition 2, therefore more glucose could leak out through the pores.

W. D. Stein performed this experiment. He found that more labeled glucose was lost from the cells in condition 1. The reorienting pore model was accepted as the more accurate model of the two in predicting red blood cell glucose exchange processes. This simple but elegant experiment illustrates a method of testing theories: determining which theory makes the most accurate prediction about the phenomena it is supposed to explain. The clearest evidence in support of one model over another can be obtained when the two competing theories predict opposite results under identical test conditions. When a carefully controlled test is performed, the theory which makes the more accurate prediction, as observed in the experiment, is the one accepted as most valid. The supported theory may, however, be faulty in some respects and additional refinement is often needed to make it more accurate in predicting and explaining smaller details of the phenomenon being observed.

We have reviewed such a study of model predictive accuracy in cell membrane facilitated diffusion.

Active Transport. Our final discussion on model building concerns active transport across cell membranes. Some living cells are known to maintain a difference in ion concentration across their membranes. In some cases sodium ions are continuously pumped out of the cell. The external sodium concentration clearly exceeds the internal concentration. Theoretically, energy is required to maintain this concentration difference by transporting ions against a concentration gradient. To test the prediction of energy requirement for active transport across membranes, sodium transport across membranes has been studied under various conditions known to inhibit metabolism. Freezing and cyanide poisoning, which are known to inhibit metabolism, also inhibited ion transport. This evidence supports a metabolic origin for active ion transport energy. The molecular mechanism of active ion transport is not fully understood. It appears likely, however, that ATPase may be a carrier molecule. This enzyme cleaves ATP, which may yield sufficient free energy to perform work in transporting ions across the cell membrane. When the cell is metabolically active, and ATP yields are sufficiently large, energy is available to actively drive ions across the membrane. If the cell is frozen or poisoned with cyanide, ATP production is stopped, and active ion transport is inhibited. This theoretical discussion supports the concept of ATPase as an ion transporting mechanism in the cell membrane.

In total, this discussion of research on cell membrane structure and function clearly illustrates the need for further empirical research on the subject. Although several models of the membrane are widely accepted, the evidence in support of any single one is far from conclusive. The widespread occurrence of membranes within the cell and their remarkable diversity of function clearly demonstrates the fundamental significance of cell membranes in maintaining the life of the cell.

Analysis of Lesson Three

This lesson on cell membrane models is intended to demonstrate the organization of an enquiry-oriented reception lesson. The content is organized to communicate knowledge of specific facts, concepts, principles, and abstractions (models) in the field of cell biology, and to illustrate various cognitive skills such as analysis of elements, extrapolation, application, synthesis, and evaluation.

The lesson begins with an analysis of the component parts and functions of a membrane. The synthesis of membrane structure and function models is demonstrated by presenting the organization of various theoretical models from currently available evidence. Methods of scientific experimentation, such as the use of labeled compounds, illustrates the application of scientific procedures to specific problems. At points in the discussion, extrapolations are made. These are predictions about membrane function derived from analysis of membrane organization. For example, the organization of the Danielli-Davson model is used to predict certain properties of solute diffusion across the membrane. Each of the models is evaluated in terms of its capacity to explain observed membrane properties and the quality of the evidence used to support it. The evidence against a model is examined in respect to strengths and weaknesses of the argument employing the negative evidence. A sense of enquiry is maintained by citing the limitations of each model and briefly describing the kind of research studies being performed to test the predictive power of a model. Where possible, the fluid nature of scientific knowledge is demonstrated by discussing the changes in our understanding of membrane organization that have arisen through gathering of new data which challenged existing models and the creation of new models to represent more accurately observed membrane functions. The lesson is largely cluster-centered in structure. The various membrane models are continuously compared and contrasted as the lesson develops. In a serial-centered lesson, each membrane model is considered in sequential order with little or no comparisons to others. There are, of course, brief serial-centered sequences within the lesson. These occur where the membrane model is being described. Here, each component is presented in a linear order without much comparative discussion. This is rather clear in the presentation of the Kavanau membrane model. In total, however, the lesson is comparative and clusters information around the relative value of the various models as explanations of membrane organization and activity.

The sequence of this lesson relative to the eight cell model is not as simple as those of the two preceding lessons. There are seven major steps in this lesson which proceed through the following sequence of categories in the eight cell model: cell 3, cell 1, cell 2, cell 1, cell 2, cell 6, and cell 4. The lesson begins with a general discussion of membrane structure with reference to the various, often contradictory, interpretations scientists have given for membrane organization. This suggests that the introduction should be classified in cell 3 (variables, structures, generalities). Thereafter, the Danielli-Davson model structure is discussed as a general cell model without variation. This segment should be classified in cell 1 (constants, structures, generalities). Then, a discussion of membrane diffusion regulation is presented. Since this is basically a discussion of general cellular processes without reference to variations in occurrence, the sequence is classified in cell 2. There follows a general discussion of mosaic membrane models with particular reference to Wallach's model.

Since this is largely a discussion of membrane structure at a general and constant level, it is classified in cell 1. This structural description is carried over into the introduction to Kavanau's model. At this point the discussion shifts to an analysis of membrane processes as the open-to-closed transitions are described. This discussion of a general cellular process as a constant feature of membrane activity warrants classification of this sequence in cell 2. The ensuing discussion of red blood cell sugar transport across the membrane is a discussion of a specific cell function presented as a constant phenomenon. It is classified as representative of cell 6. The conclusion of the lesson contains a discussion of active transport as a general process occurring under specified conditions of cellular metabolism. The variations in membrane activity are presented as a function of the metabolic state of the cell, suggesting classification of the conclusion in cell 4 of the eight cell model. In general, the sequential pattern of the lesson alternates between discussions of structures and of processes. This is indicated by the pattern of organization in the middle of the lesson where the classification alternates between cell 1 and cell 2. This was done intentionally to enhance pupil interest by moving from a discussion of static phenomena to dynamic ones. The variety of content introduced in this lesson is illustrated by the fact that five of the eight cells in the model are used in designing the lesson. This lesson is generally more diffuse than the preceding cluster-centered lesson on the topic of nucleic acids. There is no clearly identified principle or theme running through the lesson. It is thus less highly structured than the nucleic acid lesson with respect to Bruner's concept of the use of principles in providing relatedness among specific facts. There is no clearly stated advance organizer although the lesson tends to move from generalities toward specifics as Ausubel would recommend. There is little hierarchical organization. The lesson is organized to illustrate cognitive skills and to present scientific enquiry as an open-ended experience. In this context, a loosely structured organization is reasonable since it supports the major outcome objective of enhancing pupil acquisition of various diversified cognitive skills.

Lesson Four Lipid Molecular Organization: Application of Physical Principles to Biological Problems

Lipids are oily substances found in cells as food reserves and as components of cell membranes. The category of compounds called lipids includes a wide variety of fatty substances. We shall discuss some of these, namely, fatty acids, phospholipids, and cholesterol. These lipids are found in various forms as components of cell membranes. The organization of these lipids in the cell membrane can have a significant effect on the structure and function of the membrane. It is worthwhile, therefore, to study the physical properties of lipids toward a fuller appreciation of their role in cell membrane organization. It is believed that lipids are distributed in the membrane as a double layer consisting of two thin lamellae. Each lamella is one molecule thick. The study of lipid monolayer and bilayer organization is useful in understanding the physical properties of membrane lipid organization (Anderson 1970a).

Lipid Molecular Structure. Fatty acids are lipids containing a carboxyl group and a hydrocarbon chain. The carboxyl group contains oxygen atoms which make it polar (attracted to charged molecules and to water). The hydrocarbon chain has oily properties and confers a hydrophobic quality on the fatty acids. Fatty acids are classified as amphiphiles. These are compounds having both polar and non-polar groups. Phospholipids are amphiphiles containing a phosphate group. The most commonly studied phospholipid is egg lecithin which is found abundantly in egg yolk and forms a significant portion of all membrane lipids. Egg lecithin is a complex molecule containing two fatty acid molecules linked to two carbon atoms of a three-carbon glycerol molecule. The remaining carbon atom is linked to a phosphate group which in turn is bonded to a choline group. The choline group consists of two carbon atoms and a nitrogen atom containing three methyl groups.

The choline nitrogen bears a positive charge since it contains four bonds and has chemical organization equivalent to that of

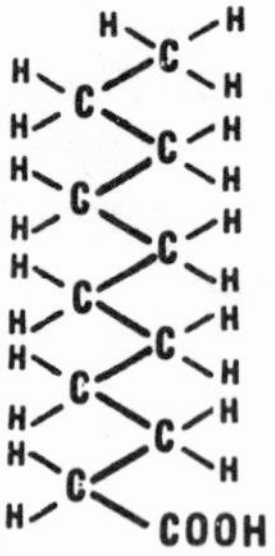

fatty acyl chains

glycerol

phosphate

choline

fatty acid

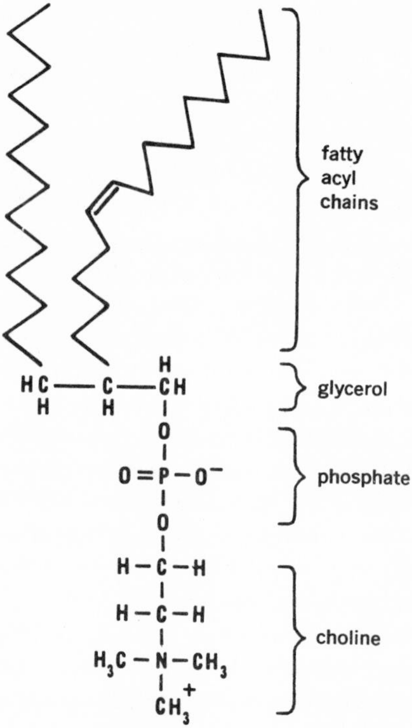

egg lecithin

an ammonium ion which bears a unitary positive charge. Egg lecithin is an amphiphile since the fatty acid chains are hydrophobic and the phosphocholine group is polar. One of the fatty acid chains may have a double bond, causing a kink in the chain. Although the chains are continuously undergoing thermomolecular motion, on the average one chain is straight and the other has a slight bend at the point of the double bond. Fatty acids and egg lecithin molecules are linear molecules particularly when closely packed near to one another. The third kind of lipid to be discussed is cholesterol. This is a multiple ring compound. There are four rings. One ring contains a hydroxyl group and the adjoining ring has a double bond in a nearby position. This molecule is also an amphiphile since it contains a hydrophobic ring and a polar hydroxyl group.

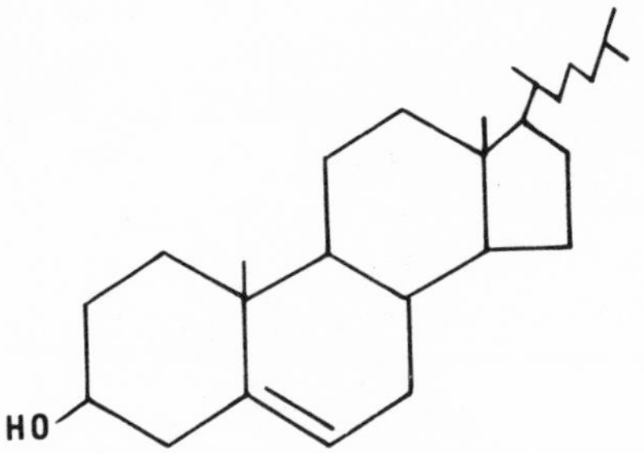

HO

cholesterol

Lipid Spherule Models of Cell Membranes. Pure egg lecithin or mixtures of egg lecithin and cholesterol can be used to simulate cell membrane lipid organization. When egg lecithin alone or a mixture of it and other lipids, is dispersed in water, spherules are formed. Each spherule is about 0.9 microns or smaller in diameter. The spherule of lipid consists of a series of concentric bilayer shells very much like the layers of tissue in an onion. Each lipid spherule layer consists of a double layer of lipid. The fatty tails of the lipid molecules are directed inward and the polar groups project outward. Each lipid bilayer is surrounded by a layer of water which is bound to the polar groups of the lipid molecules. Therefore, a cross section through such a lipid spherule would reveal alternating layers of lipid and water arranged in a concentric pattern. Thus each spherule simulates a cell. The lipid layer on the outside of the spherule is analogous to the plasma membrane surrounding a living cell. The water on the inside of the spherule simulates cytoplasm. Water outside of the spherule represents environmental water. Lipid spherules can be used to study the effects of lipid composition on the passage of molecules across cell membrane lipid layers. To do this, lipids are added to a water solution containing the molecule to be studied. Glucose molecules are often studied. The lipids are mixed with the water solution to form spherules with glucose solution trapped inside them. The untrapped glucose molecules remaining in the external solution are removed by a column-filtering method. This produces a suspension of lipid spherules containing only the trapped glucose. Thus, the rate of glucose diffusion across the lipid boundaries can be measured by determining how much leaks out into the surrounding water. In other words, the lipid spherules are small sacs of glucose solution. We can measure the rate of glucose diffusion across the membrane of the sac simply by determining how much glucose is found on the outside after a given amount of time has passed.

The kind of lipid contained in the spherule can be varied and the amount of glucose lost per unit of time can be determined. For example, one can study the effects of pure lecithin, or lecithin plus cholesterol, on the release of glucose. An experiment of this kind was performed wherein glucose was trapped in spherules composed only of egg lecithin. The membranes of these spherules contained only one kind of lipid molecule. A second group of spherules was produced by mixing egg lecithin and cholesterol in equal proportions. These spherules contained membranes having two kinds of lipids—linear lecithin molecules and ring-shaped cholesterol molecules. The rate of glucose leakage from the two spherules was compared, and it was found that the leakage was much faster from the lecithin-only spherules as compared to the lecithin-cholesterol spherules. These experiments were easily repeated, thus giving credence to the observation that the presence of cholesterol in the membrane surrounding the spherule inhibited the passage of glucose across the spherule boundary. What physical principles of lipid organization can explain this observation? What are the properties of the mixed lipid boundary as compared to the egg lecithin boundary that inhibit glucose passage? These questions and similar ones about membrane lipid organization can be partially answered by studying the properties of the lipids in thin films cast on a water surface. This field of study is called surface chemistry. The properties of lipid films one molecule thick are studied by spreading them on a water surface. Changes in tension of the water surface give evidence of the organization of the lipid in the thin layer. To fully understand the kind of studies that can be performed and the meaning of the results for biological investigations, we need to examine some of the concepts and procedures used in surface chemistry (Adams 1968).

Basic Principles of Surface Chemistry. The surface of water exists in a state of tension. At an air-water interface, surface molecules of water experience an unequal force of attraction. Each water molecule in the surface is attracted laterally to adjacent surface molecules and inwardly toward surrounding underlying molecules. There are attractive forces to either side of a surface molecule and inward away from the surface. However, there are few if any attractive forces at the air surface. Therefore each of the water molecules in the surface experiences a lateral and inward pull which is not balanced by an outward pull. The molecules are held in a state of tension much like the surface of an expanded balloon. Of course, there is constant exchange of surface water molecules with the underlying bulk phase. On the average, however, at any instant in time, the surface layer of molecules is under a tension which confers an elastic quality to the water surface. The presence of foreign molecules in the water surface disrupts the cohesive forces of attraction among the water molecules and concurrently reduces the surface tension of the water. Surface tension is measured in dynes per cm, that is, units of force per unit of length of water surface. This may seem unusual at first consideration. But, when we remember that surface tension is an expression of lateral attraction among molecules at the interface, the definition is readily explained. Consider a very fine needle one centimeter long placed in the water surface. The fine needle will experience a lateral pull perpendicular to each side. This pull or tension is measured in force units, here expressed as dynes. Therefore we see that surface tension exerts a pull perpendicular to the length of the needle. The lateral force is usually expressed in dynes per centimeter. We may replace the needle by a line of water molecules and reason that it also experiences a lateral force along its axis which can be expressed in dynes per centimeter. The surface tension is symbolized as gamma (γ). The surface tension of pure water against an air surface is about 70 dynes per centimeter. When amphiphiles such as long chain fatty acids, phospholipids, or cholesterol are added to a water surface, they do not dissolve readily into the underlying bulk phase. Rather, the molecules remain at the surface. Their polar groups (water-attracting groups) penetrate into the water, but their hydrophobic segments project into the air. The hydrocarbon chains, being oily in character, do not mix readily with the water phase. Thus, the molecules are stabilized at the air/water interface.

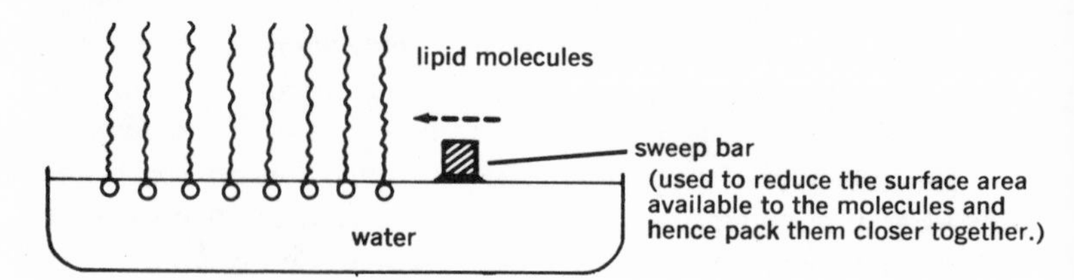

The lipid molecules float on the surface like small boats. They constantly move around on the surface undergoing continuous thermomolecular motion. The presence of the lipid molecules in the interface disrupts the lateral cohesive forces among the water molecules and the surface tension is reduced. Molecules that orient in the water surface and disrupt the intermolecular tension forces are called surface active agents. When they are present in the water surface, the surface tension is reduced below 70 dynes per centimeter. Surface tension has been reduced by the presence of the surface active molecules, and we can conceive this to be a pressure. In other words, there is a net decrease in pull on water molecules in the surface when surface active agents are present. This decrease in pull is in effect a surface pressure. A monolayer of surface active agents produces a surface pressure which is expressed as the difference in surface tension of pure water and the surface tension of water containing a surface film. If we symbolize the surface tension of pure water as γ_W and the surface tension of water with a lipid film as γ_L, then the surface pressure (π) is simply the difference between the two; namely, $\pi = \gamma_W - \gamma_L$. The pressure is, of course, measured in dynes per centimeter. The amount of surface pressure produced by a lipid film is related to the physical properties of the film and the amount of surface area available.

In general, as the surface area available to the film is reduced, the surface pressure increases. This is intuitively reasonable. As the lipid molecules in the film are pushed closer together—as they are crowded into a smaller area—they push more vigorously on the surrounding water molecules, thereby further reducing surface tension and increasing surface pressure. As a general principle, decreasing the surface area available to molecules in a film increases concurrently the surface pressure of the film. This is analogous to pressure of matter in three dimensions. If the volume occupied by a gas is reduced, the pressure of the gas increases proportionately.

The interesting property of lipid surface films is that the properties of the molecules in the film determine the rate at which surface pressure increases as area is reduced. Three curves are produced when surface pressure is plotted as a function of area available to each molecule. The curves are displayed in a pressure-area (π-A) graph. The abscissa of the graph is marked in units of area. In this case we must use square angstroms ($Å^2$) since we are expressing the area as surface area available per molecule. Each molecule occupies a very small area, indeed. Therefore, we

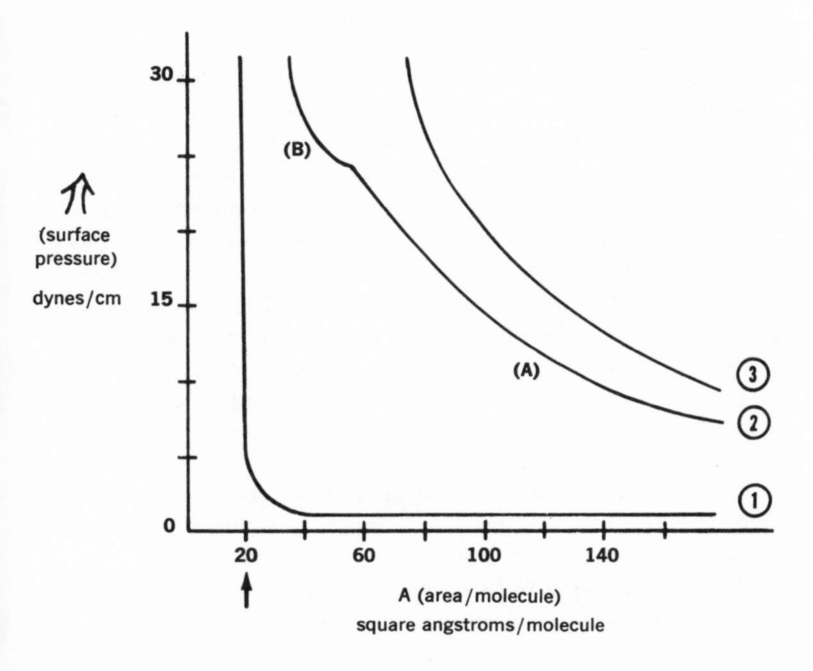

must use very small area units. The ordinate is marked in pressure units—dynes/cm.

Curve 1 is produced by a surface film composed of highly cohesive surface active lipids. Since the lipids tend to clump as small patches on the surface of the water, particularly as liquid cools and condenses on solid surfaces, the film is called a *condensed film.* The condensed film curve, as you can see, shows very little change in surface pressure as the area is decreased from relatively large values. The surface pressure remains low across a broad range of area reduction. Suddenly, however, a reduced area is reached at about 40 square angstroms where the pressure curve begins to rise abruptly. This is easily understood when we consider the physical properties of the film. Most of the surface active molecules are clumped in small patches on the water surface very much like groups of closely spaced boats on a pond surface. Now as the surface area is reduced by pushing the molecules closer together, they do not exert much pressure until the clumps begin to collide with one another; and then, as the area is reduced further, they press against the water surface considerably and each reduction in area sharply increases the surface pressure. The final pronounced and abrupt rise in curve 1 is due to pressing together of the patches of lipid into a solid film with tight packing of the molecules.

For contrast, we consider curve 3 next. Pressure increases gradually as the area is decreased. There is appreciable pressure even at large areas and the curve is a long sweeping one, showing continuous increase with decrease in area. This is called a gaseous curve since it is produced by molecules that tend to disperse themselves on the water surface. The molecules are only slightly cohesive and do not clump on the water surface. The constant molecular motion of the molecules on the water surface causes them to collide and bound away from one another thus producing some pressure even at large surface areas. One may consider gaseous surface films as analogous to three dimensional gaseous states of matter. Gas molecules undergo continuous molecular motion and produce pressure by constant collision among themselves and with the walls of their container. A gaseous film produces the same effect in two dimensions. Gaseous molecules usually are not cohesive—either because their polar groups are charged, causing mutual repulsion among the molecules, or their hydrocarbon chains are too short to allow close adlineation of the chains. Long hydrocarbon chains favor the mutual attraction of surface molecules through Van der Waals forces of attraction. Thus, long chain surface molecules become cohesive since their hydrocarbon chains can make contact along a large surface. We may think of them as being "sticky" for one another. Short chain molecules do not have this property. Short chain molecules and those with charged polar groups tend to form gaseous surface films. Long chain molecules and those without charged groups tend to be cohesive and form condensed surface films as shown by curve 1.

Curve 2 represents a surface film which is intermediate in state between condensed and gaseous. It is called an expanded surface film. By inspection of the graph, you learn that the curve contains two parts. At high surface areas, the right-hand part of the curve (A) is gaseous. It forms a long sweeping trace. Thereafter, the left-hand part (B) at lower surface areas is a condensed curve. There is little change in surface pressure as the area is decreased until a point is reached where the pressure rises quite abruptly. What does this curve tell us? It shows that molecules in an expanded surface film tend to be repulsed at high surface areas; they form a gaseous phase on the water surface. As surface area is decreased, however, a point is reached at which molecules are pressed against one another and they condense into small patches. That is, the molecules are no longer repulsed when they reach a certain critical state of packing. At that point their attractive forces overcome the repulsive forces and the molecules begin to coalesce. The coalescence continues as the surface area is reduced, thereby stabilizing the surface pressure. However, a point is ultimately reached where all of the molecules have coalesced and further area reductions produce sharp rise in pressure as the solid film is put under compression.

Lecithin and Cholesterol Monolayers. The pressure-area curve produced by a lipid film indicates the properties of the molecules in the film. Lipids with long hydrocarbon chains containing one or more double bonds (as in egg lecithin) produce gaseous films. They are not condensed since the double bond causes a kink in the hydrocarbon chain as explained earlier and prevents close association of the molecules. Lipids with double bonds tend to form gaseous films since the cohesive forces among the molecules are effective only at short distances. The double bond alters the linear configuration of the hydrocarbon chain and prevents close association of the molecules. Surface chemists use a clever technique to verify that the double bond is the cause of the gaseous state in the film. Synthetic lecithin is a molecule with identical structure to egg lecithin except that synthetic lecithin has no double bond in the hydrocarbon chain. When synthetic lecithin is spread as a film on a water surface, it forms a condensed film. Since the only change in structure is the double bond, we can conclude that it is the double bond in egg lecithin that causes it to form a gaseous film. In the absence of a double bond, analogous molecules form condensed films. Cholesterol forms condensed films. The almost planar set of rings in the cholesterol molecule allow sufficiently close packing that the molecules tend to coalesce into patches. The patches float around on the water surface and do not exert pressure until they are closely packed upon each other.

The area occupied by a molecule on a water surface can be determined using surface chemistry techniques.

Molecular Surface Area. We make use of pressure-area curves to obtain a measure of the minimum area occupied by a molecule. The point on the curve where maximum pressure is produced represents the point of film compression at which all of the molecules are packed so closely together that they occupy the smallest possible space. At this point on the abscissa, we can read the area occupied by each molecule in square angstroms. In curve 1, the molecules in a condensed film become solidly packed against one another at approximately 20 square angstroms of surface area/molecule. The arrow marks the coordinate on the abscissa. We conclude, therefore, that the area occupied by each molecule at closest packing is 20 square angstroms. Molecules in gaseous films clearly occupy larger areas than molecules in condensed films. In the example shown in curve 3, the final limiting area is about 60 square angstroms per molecule for closest packing of gaseous molecules. If the molecules are pressed any closer together, the film becomes unstable and collapses into the underlying water phase.

Thus far we have discussed surface films composed of one kind of lipid at a time. What information can we obtain by putting two or more kinds of lipids on the water surface at the same time? The pressure-area curves of a mixed lipid film should tell us whether there are mutual influences of the molecules upon one another. For example, if one places a mixture of cholesterol and egg lecithin on a water surface, the film is condensed, showing that the cholesterol reduces the gaseous state of the egg lecithin when the two are combined on the water surface. Additional information can be obtained about the organization of the molecules in the mixed lipid film. If we place equal proportions of two molecules on a water surface, and if the two molecules occupy areas independent of one another, then we would expect the average area occupied by each molecule to be the arithmetic average of their individual molecular areas as measured in a pure lipid film. For example, assume a lecithin molecule occupies 60 square angstroms area when present in a pure lecithin film, and a cholesterol molecule occupies 40 square angstroms area when in a pure cholesterol film. Now if we make a mixed film by adding equal numbers of cholesterol and lecithin molecules on the water surface, we should expect to find that the pressure-area curve for this combination shows an average area per molecule as $60+40/2=50$ square angstroms. If, however, the molecules interact with one another in some way that prevents their areas from adding proportionately, then we might expect to find a deviation from the expected average value of 50 square angstroms.

Interaction of Lecithin and Cholesterol. When equal numbers of cholesterol and egg lecithin molecules are spread on a water surface, there is a deviation from the expected value for their combined areas. The average area obtained from the pressure-area curve is much less than the expected 50 square angstroms. This shows that egg lecithin and cholesterol interact to produce a

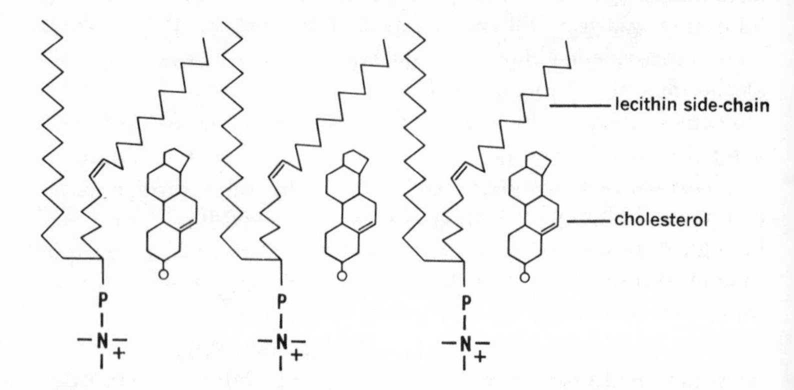

reduced surface area occupied by the mixture. How can we explain this? One theoretical answer is that the double bond in the egg lecithin forms an arch in the side chain of the molecule. Under this arch is sufficient space for the cholesterol molecule. Two molecules take up less space than expected. The cholesterol is sitting under the arching side chain of the egg lecithin. If this hypothesis is valid, then a mixture of *synthetic* lecithin and cholesterol should not deviate from the expected average area per molecule. Synthetic lecithin has no double bond and therefore cannot form an arch to accommodate the cholesterol molecule. The two kinds of molecules should sit side by side and occupy nearly the same additive area. When films are made of synthetic lecithin and cholesterol, the area is found to be additive. That is, the pressure-area curves show that synthetic lecithin and cholesterol do not interact. Therefore, it is a logical conclusion that egg lecithin interacts with cholesterol by providing a space under its side chain for the cholesterol.

Now we are in a position to answer the question, why are egg lecithin spherules readily permeable to glucose whereas spherules made of egg lecithin and cholesterol are less permeable? The egg lecithin forms a gaseous film with intermolecular spaces. Glucose can diffuse between the lecithin molecules. Egg lecithin and cholesterol surface films are more compact, the cholesterol occupies the spaces between the lecithin molecules, and reduces the space available for glucose diffiusion. In simple terms, cholesterol blocks the pores in the lecithin spherule membrane, thereby inhibiting glucose diffusion. These data suggest that cellular membranes rich in cholesterol would be stabilized by the presence of the cholesterol in the molecular spaces between the lecithin molecules and would reduce the rate of molecular diffusion across the membrane.

This example illustrates vividly the remarkable precision one can obtain in applying surface chemistry techniques to molecular biological problems. The use of surface chemistry in modern biological research is one of the new frontiers in scientific enquiry (Shah and Schulman 1967).

Analysis of Lesson Four

The purpose of this lesson is to communicate knowledge of lipid chemistry and demonstrate the application of physical principles to solving biological problems. It is a reception lesson containing a mixture of serial-centered and cluster-centered sequences within the lesson. The lesson is initiated with a serial-centered discussion of each major lipid component of the cell membrane. The attributes of each lipid are presented to completion before the next lipid is described. Thereafter, a cluster-centered discussion follows wherein the various lipids are interrelated as to their roles as components of lipid spherules simulating cell membranes. Following this discussion, a serial-centered sequence is presented on the subject of lipid monolayers cast on water surfaces. The various concepts in surface chemistry are set forth in sequential order. The lesson concludes with a cluster-centered discussion beginning with the description of mixed lipid films on page 151 and extending to the end of the lesson. The sequential organization of the lesson with reference to the eight cell model is somewhat more complex than that of previous lessons on biological topics. Most of the data in this lesson is physical and chemical. Therefore we need to set forth some rules for application of the eight cell model to this lesson. First, the specifics-to-generalities dimension means a discussion of specific molecules, compounds, or atoms versus a general discussion of a class of molecules, compounds, or atoms. The general discussion might include rare gases or alkaline earth elements, for example. Thus, if we are discussing the properties of lipids, we are discussing generalities. If, however, a discussion of a specific molecule is presented, such as a description of cholesterol, lecithin, or glucose, that constitutes a presentation of specifics. The structures-to-processes dimension is used to distinguish descriptions of static states, such as the area occupied by a molecule on a surface or its molecular organization (structure), from the dynamic events occurring when molecules interact (processes). Thus, the position of molecules on a water surface is a structure category. The movement and interaction of molecules is a process. Finally, any discussion of a phenomenon which presents the data as a non-varying or unchangeable occurrence is classified as a presentation of constants. On the other hand, a discussion of variations in organization or processes as a function of some influence, internal or external to the system being described, constitutes a presentation of variables. We are now ready to describe the sequential organization of this lesson using the eight cell model.

There is a brief introductory discussion of the organization of lipids in cell membranes; this is classified in cell 1 of the eight cell model. The next section concerns the description of various specific lipid molecules. The constant structural features of these molecules are presented (cell 5). Thereafter, an extended discussion of lecithin spherules as models of cell membrane is presented. The process of glucose diffusion across lecithin boundaries is discussed. This constitutes a discussion of constant specific processes (cell 6). A general discussion of surface chemistry is presented including the interaction among various kinds of lipids in forming gaseous, expanded, and condensed films. Since no specific class of lipids is discussed and considerable attention is devoted to the molecular activities of the lipids producing the various kinds of surface films, this segment of the lesson is classified as cell 4 (variables, processes, generalities). The discussion is one of variables since the various effects of double bonds and ring formation on the molecular activities of the lipids are discussed. Then a discussion of specific kinds of molecules (lecithin and cholesterol) in surface films is presented. This is classified in cell 6. The general description of surface area occupied by a molecule is classified as cell 1. Since no particular molecule is being discussed, this section of the lesson is concerned with generalities. Finally, the lesson concludes with a discussion of specific molecules (lecithin and cholesterol) with reference to their interaction in monolayers and bilayers and the effect of this interaction on glucose diffusion across lipid spherule membranes (cell 8). The sequential order of the lesson in terms of the eight cell model is 1, 5, 6, 4, 6, 1, 8. This is a richly divergent lesson utilizing five of the eight cells in the model. Over half of the five cells used are from the lower half of the model (5, 6, 8) which contains the cells on specifics.

Lesson Five The Cell: Unit of Structure and Function

Biologists have recognized for some time that the organization and activity of cells reflects in large measure the structure and function of the total organism. Early cytological studies clearly demonstrated that all living things were composed of cells and that cells could be considered the building blocks of life. The apparent integrity of the cell as the fundamental unit of life in the eyes of early biologists should not be underestimated. Modern molecular research on cell structure and function has sometimes been so fragmented and specialized as to almost obscure the remarkable degree of integration of structure and function of various components in the living cell. However, the great precision with which modern biological research has defined the role of each individual cellular component in maintaining the life of the cell now allows us to synthesize a sophisticated model of the cell as a unit assembly. The orderliness of the cellular components and the synergistic mechanisms that have evolved to coordinate and interconnect cellular processes are worthy of greater attention than they have received heretofore. As a means of gathering sufficient data to build a unified model of the cell, we discuss individual cellular organelles and their functions as best determined by modern molecular research. These separate descriptions are unified in a general model.

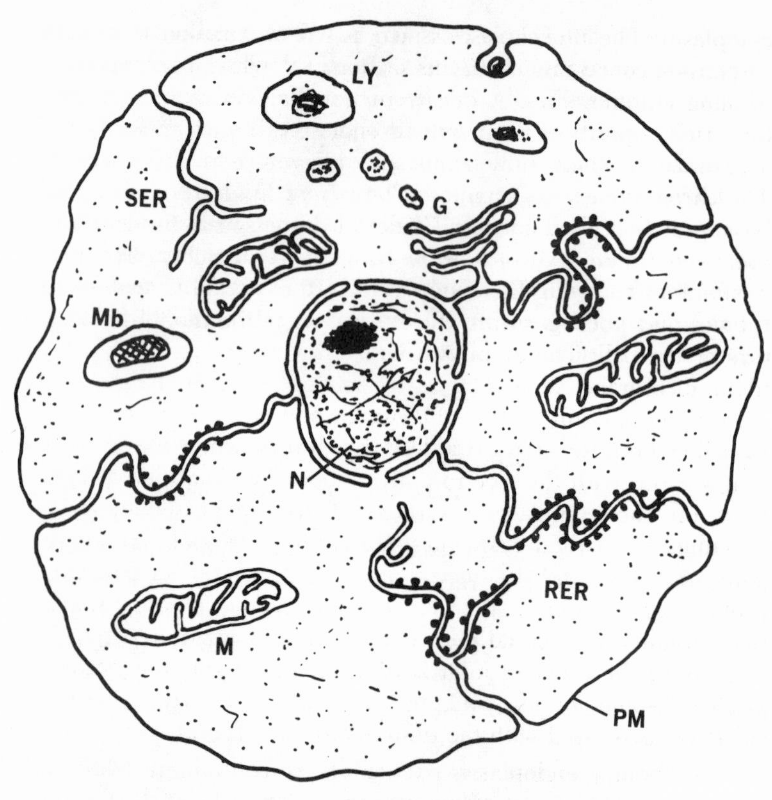

Figure 20 A General Model of the Cell

G	Golgi body	N	Nucleus
Ly	Lysosome	PM	Plasma Membrane
M	Mitochondrion	RER	Rough Endoplasmic Reticulum
Mb	Microbody	SER	Smooth Endoplasmic Reticulum

Cell Organelles. There are several major cell organelles we need to describe in preparing the model. They are: nucleus, endoplasmic reticulum, Golgi apparatus, lysosomes, plasma membrane, mitochondrion, microbody, and soluble enzymes.

The nucleus is a prominently visible cellular organelle when viewed with the light or electron microscope. It is surrounded by a double membrane containing pores that provide continuity between the nucleoplasm within the nucleus and the surrounding cytoplasm. The nucleoplasm is composed of a colloidal protein suspension containing clearly identifiable strands of nucleoprotein forming chromosomes. A denser body called the nucleolus contains rich deposits of ribonucleoprotein and characteristically has a granular or sometimes laminated appearance in cross-section. The chromosomes are composed largely of DNA and associated basic proteins called histones. The nuclear membrane is at various points continuous with an elaborate network of intracytoplasmic membranes known as the endoplasmic reticulum. This network of tubules and pockets forms the internal membranous superstructure of the cell. There are two categories of endoplasmic reticulum membrane segments: rough endoplasmic reticulum and smooth endoplasmic reticulum. Rough endoplasmic reticulum is so called because of its studded appearance when observed in thin sections with the electron microscope. The knob-like projections on the cytoplasmic surface of the rough endoplasmic reticulum are called ribosomes. Ribosomes are globular aggregates of protein and ribonucleic acid. These are the sites of most protein biosynthesis in the cell. Each ribosome is composed of two subunits of unequal size. One subunit is about 140 by 170 angstroms; the other subunit is 95 angstroms by 170 angstroms. Each ribosome subunit contains an internal core where most of the RNA associated with the ribosome is to be found.

The rough endoplasmic reticulum is continuous with the smooth endoplasmic reticulum. Its membrane surfaces do not contain ribosomes and therefore appear smooth in the electron microscope. The smooth endoplasmic reticulum is continuous with a closely spaced stack of membranous sacs called the Golgi apparatus. The Golgi apparatus forms a system of flattened sacs whose peripheral margins are dilated to form bulbous vesicles called Golgi saccules. The saccules sometimes pinch off as free cytoplasmic vesicles. If the vesicles contain hydrolytic (degradative) enzymes, they are called lysosomes. A lysosome is a vacuole whose function is digestion. Lysosomes are described according to their shape, functional history in the cell, and contents. Lysosomes may be pinched off directly from the endoplasmic reticulum as well as from the Golgi appartus. The endoplasmic reticulum membranes are continuous with the plasma membrane which surrounds the cell. The plasma membrane is a thin lipoprotein envelope which regulates the passage of material into and out of the cell, contains the cellular soluble molecules within the cell, and delimits the cytoplasm from the non-living environment. The plasma membrane sometimes invaginates to form pocket-like intrusions. When these pinch off internally to form vacuoles containing sequestered food, they are called phagosomes or food vacuoles. The plasma membrane may also form thin canal-like intrusions which end in a *cul de sac* where small vacuoles are pinched off to form pinocytic vesicles. These vesicles often contain liquid-suspended droplets of food. The vacuoles and vesicles so formed by phagocytosis and pinocytosis are surrounded by a single membrane. There are other membranous organelles. The mitochondria are globose structures surrounded by a double membrane. The outer membrane is smooth and sac-like. The inner separate membrane is folded and forms intricate pockets called cristae. Cristae contain small knob-like projections on their surface called elementary particles. The elementary particles are in fact projections on the surface of membrane units. Each membrane unit is probably dumbbell shaped, the basal portion being cuboidal and forming the membrane envelope through close packing with adjacent units. The upper globose portion forms the elementary particle attached to the membrane.

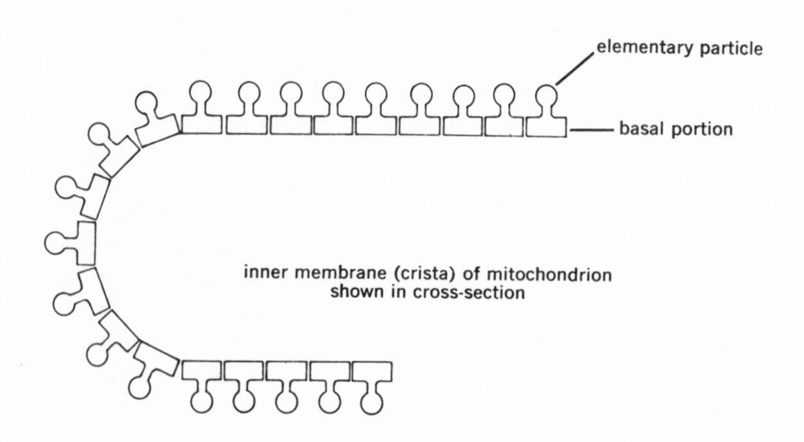

The mitochondrion is predominately responsible for the metabolic conversion of food substances into high energy chemical compounds such as ATP. Fatty acid elongation and degradation also occurs in the mitochondrion.

The microbody is a single membrane-bound organelle sometimes containing a granular inclusion. Oxidative enzymes such as peroxidase, urate oxidase, and hydroxy acid oxidases are bound in this organelle. It has sometimes been called the extramitochondrial site of oxidation in the cell. It is believed that, among other functions, the microbody detoxifies harmful waste products such as peroxides and lactic acid. Aside from the membrane-bound organelles, there are numerous enzymes suspended in the cytoplasm of the cell. These catalytic proteins, being soluble, float around in the cytoplasm and facilitate the biosynthesis of essential molecules to maintain cellular structure and function.

Cell Organelle Function. Each of the aforementioned organelles is discussed in greater detail now, giving particularly the functions of each. The nucleus is the center of control for cell function, although we must acknowledge that the flow of control is two-way between the nucleus and the cytoplasm. The nucleus is, however, central as an initiator of cellular control. The chromatin (DNA) in the nucleus contains coded information to direct protein synthesis. The information is transmitted from the DNA to ribosomes by an information-carrying molecule called messenger RNA (mRNA). mRNA leaves the nucleus by way of the nuclear membrane pores. The messenger RNA is a polymer composed of sub units called nucleotides—a feature it shares with DNA. The sequence of nucleotides is the locus of information storage. When mRNA unites with a ribosome, a series of events are initiated whereby protein sub units called amino acids are linked to form a protein. The individual bonds linking the amino acids to each other are called peptides; the whole protein is called a polypeptide. mRNA dictates the sequence of amino acids in a polypeptide. The rough endoplasmic reticulum is the major site of enzyme synthesis and structural protein synthesis—both being the products of a process initiated and controlled by DNA. The enzymes produced at the rough endoplasmic reticulum are either anabolic enzymes which regulate build up of cellular molecules or catabolic enzymes catalyzing the break down of cellular material and ingested food. Some, if not most, of these catabolic enzymes migrate from the rough endoplasmic reticulum through the smooth endoplasmic reticulum and concentrate in the Golgi apparatus. The Golgi apparatus serves as a packaging center. Catabolic enzymes called hydrolases are collected in the peripheral saccules of the Golgi. These saccules pinch off to form lysosomes. These newly formed lysosomes are called primary lysosomes since they have not yet entered into the digestive process in which they are destined to participate. Primary lysosomes often appear as densely granular vacuoles. The hydrolases, being abundant and concentrated in a small volume, no doubt contribute to the optical density of the lysosome. Once the primary lysosome has been formed, it migrates into the cytoplasm. The vital organelles of the cell are protected from the degradative action of the enzymes by the membrane surrounding the lysosome. The lysosomes perform two major functions: they (1) digest engulfed food, and (2) destroy senescent and damaged cell organelles. The first function is called phagotrophy and the second is called autophagy. Phagotrophy begins when the plasma membrane engulfs food particles to form phagosomes. These food vacuoles move through the cytoplasm until they encounter a primary lysosome. Then, by a process not fully understood, the two vacuoles fuse. The hydrolases are emptied into the food vacuole and digestion of the food begins. The vacuole formed by the fusion of a primary lysosome and a phagosome is called a secondary lysosome. The engulfed food is broken down into its constituent molecules. Carbohydrates are cleaved to yield individual sugar molecules such as glucose. Proteins are eventually degraded to form amino acids. Nucleic acid polymers are degraded to form nucleotides, and fats are broken down to yield fatty acids. Most of these usable molecules move into the cytoplasm. The remaining material inside the lysosome is largely debris and the whole body is called a residual vacuole. In protozoa, the residual debris is defecated by extrusion through the plasma membrane. At this point we should mention that in addition to vacuolar uptake of food, the plasma membrane also has carrier molecules which transport sugars and ions into the cell. These mechanisms of nutrient uptake are regulated by feedback control mechanisms to ensure the proper flow of food into the cell.

Mitochondria are centers of cellular respiration. Here oxygen is consumed, carbon dioxide is formed as a waste product, and energy rich molecules are produced. ATP (adenosine triphosphate) is the major high energy compound synthesized in the mitochondrion. ATP molecules move from the mitochondria throughout the cell to provide chemical energy required for synthesis reactions in the cell. The process of respiration consists of three steps: (1) glycolytic degradation of glucose (sugar) to a two carbon product; some ATP is produced at this step; (2) oxidative breakdown of the three-carbon fragment to yield hydrogen atoms and CO_2 in the Krebs cycle; and (3) transport of the electrons from the hydrogen atoms through a series of coupled oxidation-reduction reactions where the energy yield at each step is used to synthesize ATP. This oxidation-reduction pathway is called the respiratory chain. The final step is the reduction of oxygen to form water.

Glycolysis begins with the breakdown of glucose to form two molecules of phosphoglyceraldehyde (3-carbon molecule). Two molecules of ATP are required for this reaction. Each of these phosphoglyceraldehyde molecules undergoes further transformations to yield pyruvic acid. During this process, two ATP molecules are produced for each yield of a glyceraldehyde-3-phosphate molecule. Since there are two molecules produced from each glucose molecule the gross yield is four ATP molecules. However, since two ATP molecules were used at the outset, the net yield is only *two* ATP molecules. The production of ATP during glycolysis is called substrate-level phosphorylation since the ATP is produced directly from the substrate. Enzymes are of course required to mediate the transfer of phosphate from the substrate to ADP to produce ATP. The pyruvic acid product is decarboxylated to yield a two-carbon molecule called active acetaldehyde. This molecule is sometimes called acetyl-co A to indicate that the acetate is carried by a coenzyme. Acetyl-co A enters the Krebs cycle by interacting with oxaloacetate to produce a six-carbon molecule—citrate. The coenzyme A molecule is cleaved from the acetate in this step. The citrate molecule undergoes a series of reactions resulting in the loss of two carbons as carbon dioxide and the transfer of hydrogen atoms to carrier molecules. The result of these reactions is to yield again oxaloacetate. Therefore, the Krebs cycle is a cyclic process since the initial reacting molecule (oxaloacetate) is regenerated at each completion of the cycle. We must remember that the Krebs cycle reactions are taking place on mitochondrial membranes or in the spaces between the two membranes surrounding the mitochondrion. The carbon dioxide produced in the Krebs cycle reaction is a waste product which diffuses out of the mitochondrion and out of the cell. The hydrogen-carrying molecules, however, have potential to yield high energy compounds through transfer of the chemical energy in the covalent bonds. The hydrogen-carrying molecules give up an electron from the hydrogen atom to the first molecule in the respiratory chain. The electron is transferred from one electron carrier molecule to the next in the chain of molecules. As the electron is transferred, the electron donor is oxidized and the electron acceptor is reduced. This reaction sequence is called a coupled oxidation-reduction reaction. The oxidation of one molecule (electron loss) is accomplished by a direct transfer of the electron to a second molecule which is thereby reduced. At three points in the respiratory chain, the energy yield of the oxidation-reduction reaction is used to produce an ATP molecule. The energy is used to link an ADP molecule with a phosphate to produce ATP. Three molecules of ATP are produced by the passage of one electron through the respiratory chain. There are many electrons obtained from each glucose molecule entering the mitochondrion, and there are 36 molecules of ATP produced in the breakdown of glucose. The energy in an ATP molecule can be used to drive many kinds of reactions in the cell. It is little wonder that the mitochondrion has been called the "power house" of the cell.

Toxic side products of cellular reactions must be removed if the vitality of the cell is to be maintained. Lactic acid, alcohol, and peroxides are believed to be detoxified in the microbody. This organelle has only recently been identified and its enzyme complement determined. Biochemical evidence suggests that molecules such as lactic acid (L-α-hydroxy acids) are oxidized in the microbody to yield keto acids such as pyruvic acid, and that alcohols are oxidized to aldehydes. Some of these molecules can be used in cellular respiration and in lipid synthesis. Perioxide is reduced to form water. In general, the microbody may be considered the recycling center of the cell since many toxic molecules are transformed into biologically useful molecules. The enzymes suspended in the soluble phase of the cell enhance various biosynthetic reactions. Amino acid activating enzymes which prepare amino acids for linkage in a polypeptide, nucleic acid synthesizing enzymes, fatty acid synthesizing enzymes, glycolysis enzymes, and glycogen synthesizing and degradative enzymes are found in the soluble phase. The aforementioned organelles and their functions will be interrelated in a general model.

A Model of Cell Organelle Interactions. The nucleus produces DNA and mRNA by assembling nucleotide polymers on existing DNA templates. The synthesis of nucleotide polymers requires activated nucleotides. The triphosphorylated nucleotides such as adenosine triphosphate, thymidine triphosphate, guanosine triphosphate, uridine triphosphate, and cytidine triphosphate are activated through energy released in the mitochondrion. This is shown in the model by arrows directed from the mitochondrion to the nucleus.

Messenger RNA produced in the nucleus passes to the endoplasmic reticulum to direct protein synthesis. Enzymes necessary to synthesize DNA and RNA polymers are produced here. Basic proteins diffuse to the nucleus to combine with nucleic acids. Basic proteins (histones) may regulate DNA production of mRNA by binding to various parts of the DNA helix thereby inhibiting mRNA synthesis. The histones can be thought of as regulatory proteins. Thus we see that although DNA is the primary site of information storage, proteins may regulate the transmission of the information. Some of the proteins produced in the endoplasmic reticulum are structural proteins for the synthesis of various cellular organelles. For example, cytochrome c, used in the mitochondrial respiratory chain, is synthesized by the rough endoplasmic

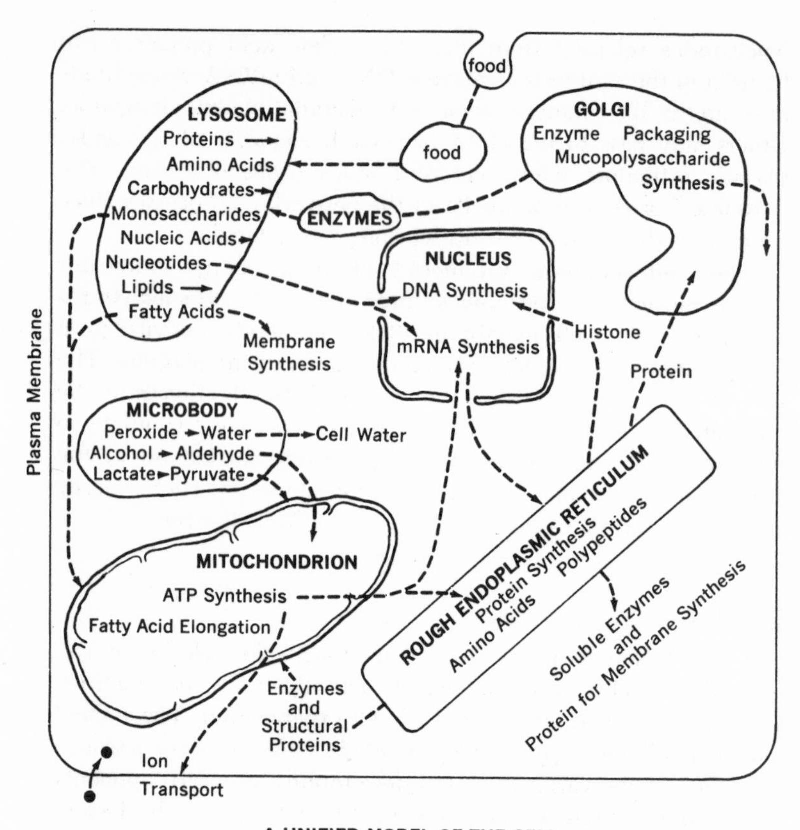

A UNIFIED MODEL OF THE CELL

reticulum. Hydrolases are synthesized at the endoplasmic reticulum and are transported to the Golgi complex where primary lysosomes are formed. The protein for mucopolysaccharide synthesis also originates at the endoplasmic reticulum. The union of protein and carbohydrate occurs in the Golgi apparatus. Primary lysosomes unite with phagosomes produced by the plasma membrane engulfment of food. The food is broken down in the lysosome to form short chain polypeptides which are degraded to amino acids. Amino acids become incorporated into polypeptides at the endoplasmic reticulum. Sugars released by hydrolytic action may enter the respiratory process thus eventually being carried as smaller molecules into the mitochondrion.

Nucleotides released from ingested nucleic acid polymers can be used in the synthesis of nuclear DNA and mRNA. Some lipids may go to the mitochondrion for degradation or elongation. Others may pass to the Golgi or smooth elements of the endoplasmic reticulum where complex lipids are synthesized. The lysosome is a central organelle in the network of processes since it provides the building blocks for complex molecules.

The mitochondrion produces ATP as an energy source for various biosynthetic reactions and for active ion and sugar transport across the cell membrane. The microbody activity as a detoxifying and recycling organelle is shown in the diagram. The several generalized functions of the cell clearly illustrate the integrated activity of its various components. They simulate in microscale the various integrative processes carried on at the organismic level, namely, regulation, ingestion, digestion, energy utilization, and detoxification (Anderson 1970b, Bourne).

Analysis of Lesson Five

This lesson is intended to communicate knowledge of cell organelle structure and function. It also illustrates the cognitive steps used in creating a model of cell organization. The unified model of cellular organization presented at the end of the lesson is a product of the various isolated descriptions of cell components and their functions as presented in the first part of the lesson. Whereas the last part of the lesson is devoted to synthesis of a model, the first part of the lesson is analytical. The various components (elements) of the cell are identified and described. The first three-quarters of the lesson are organized in a serial-centered mode and the last quarter, in which the various cellular organelles are interrelated, is cluster-centered in its organization. The cluster-centered organization begins on page 163 under the heading *A Model of Cell Organelle Interactions*. Following the introduction to the lesson, a cascaded-chain pattern is used to organize the remainder of the lesson. The cascaded-chain pattern begins on page 156 where the various cell organelles are listed. This list constitutes the first chain in the cascaded series. The next chain consists of a description of each organelle's structure. The description is presented in the same sequential order as the initial list of organelles. Following the second chain, a third one is presented which relates the functions of each organelle to its structure. The order of presentation of each organelle is the same as in the first and second chains. A careful examination of the general organization of the lesson verifies the cascaded arrangement of the content. The conclusion of the lesson follows the general sequential order of the previous parts of the lesson, but interrelates the functions of the various cell organelles within this general sequence.

The lesson is divided into two major steps based on the eight cell model. The first half of the lesson is a discussion of the structures within a general model of the cell. Therefore, this content should be classified in cell 1 of the eight cell model. The second half of the lesson contains a presentation of cellular functions at a constant and general level, indicating that it be classified in cell 2. In overview, the lesson proceeds from fundamental and concrete descriptions of cellular organelles toward greater abstraction. It culminates in a model which integrates and subsumes content presented earlier in the lesson.

Lesson Six Information and Control in Biological Systems

With recognition of the complexity of biological systems at all levels of organization—cell, tissue, organ, and organism—biologists are turning to theories of information and control as a way of understanding the regulation and coordination of biological activities (Giese; Howland). In simple terms, information is the capacity to bring about change in a system. Information is usually transmitted as a signal from a source to a receiver. The signal is carried to the receiver by a channel. Consider as an example a telephone message. The person making a call is the source of information, the telephone wires are the channel and the person to whom the call is placed is the receiver. The signal sent from source to receiver qualifies as information only if the signal causes a response in the receiver. If there is no new input transmitted by the signal, then no information has been gained by receiving the signal. Information can assume many forms. Certainly words are only one example of information signals. In cells, chemical pathways, molecules, and changes in membrane potential are examples of information carriers. At the tissue and organ level, hormones and changes in pressure and composition of the blood influence biological activity. The activity of the total organism is coordinated by a network of nerve cells carrying electrical impulses which clearly qualify as information signals. Information flow can be uni-directional or bi-directional. In a uni-directional information flow, a signal is sent from a source to a receiver where changes in activity are produced by the signal. No feedback signal is sent from the receiver to the source. In bi-directional information flow, a signal is sent from a source to a receiver. The receiver in turn changes its activity which feeds back to the source thereby coordinating the information output with its effects. The feedback signal may be positive or negative. In positive feedback, the receiver of a signal sends back information which increases the output of the signal. In negative feedback, the receiver sends information back to the source which reduces signal output. Negative feedback mechanisms are much more common in biological systems than are positive feedback mechanisms. Feedback mechanisms allow fine control of processes. The rate of a process and the kind of materials flowing through the pathway can be controlled by feedback signals from the products to the initial steps in a reaction pathway. We discuss various forms of information flow and control mechanisms at the cellular, tissue, and organismic levels of biological organization.

Enzyme Feedback Control. Some cellular biosynthetic pathways are under feedback control. In most cases the regulation of flow through the pathway is accomplished by inhibition or activation of various enzymes, catalyzing key steps in the chemical pathway. To further understand the details of enzyme control, we need to discuss the structure and activity of enzymes.

An enzyme is a biological molecule catalyzing a specific reaction. At some place on the surface of the enzyme molecule there is a special organization of atoms called the active center. This is the site on the enzyme where reactions are catalyzed. The organization of the active center is very important in determining the activity of the enzyme. If the shape of the enzyme molecule changes and disturbs the organization of the atomic groups in the active center, the activity of the enzyme is reduced. One theory of enzyme regulation assumes that enzyme activity is controlled by changing the enzyme conformation. According to this theory each enzyme has at least two binding sites. One is the active center and the other is an effector site. An effector site contains a group of atoms on the surface of the enzyme that binds an effector molecule. When the effector molecule attaches to the enzyme surface, its conformation changes. An effector can be either an activator or an inhibitor. An activator is a molecule that changes the organization of an enzyme enhancing its catalytic activity. Under these circumstances the enzyme is not active until the effector binds to it. Effectors may also be inhibitors. These molecules reduce the activity of an enzyme when they bind to its surface. In other words, the changes in conformation of the enzyme produces a distortion of the active center reducing its catalytic activity. These changes in enzyme conformation and the resulting influences on enzyme activity are called allosteric control mechanisms. What we have described thus far is a general mechanism of enzyme action and regulation. We need now to relate these mechanisms to specific biosynthetic pathways as a means of applying information theory to their analysis.

The cell contains numerous biosynthetic pathways whose products are sometimes the reactants in other pathways. To maintain the proper balance of reactants and products in a cell, special control mechanisms are required to keep the flow of materials in a pathway at a proper rate. One mechanism is feedback control. The end product of a biosynthetic pathway inhibits an enzyme in the early steps of the pathway. Consider a linear pathway without branches containing four steps, A→B→C→D. The product D is the result of several transformations of a molecule starting at A. An enzyme is used at each step to catalyze the transformation as shown by an arrow. Now suppose the product molecule D is an inhibitor of the first enzyme catalyzing the step between A and B. If the concentration of D becomes large, then the first step is inhibited and no further production of D occurs. When D is used up in other reactions and its concentration de-

A ⟶ B ⟶ C ⟶ D

creases, the inhibition of step A→B is reduced, and the flow begins again. We can treat this as an information flow problem with negative feedback. Information is flowing from A to D in the form of molecules being transformed by enzymatic action. The product concentration D acts as a feedback signal to the enzyme catalyzing the first step in the pathway. By this feedback loop organization, the concentration of D is maintained at a fairly constant and optimal level.

The organization of feedback control becomes more complicated when the pathway branches. In this case there is more than one product from a pathway. It is obvious that the products,

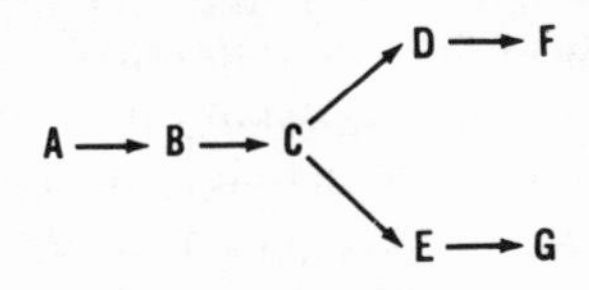

such as F, of one branch should not have complete feedback control over the pathway. Otherwise, if F became highly concentrated and inhibited step A→B, product G would also be suppressed. The product G may be essential for pathways quite independent of F. Therefore, some provision must be made to assure that no single product in a branching pathway can completely control the productivity of the sequence. There are four ways of obtaining the necessary differential feedback control: (1) multiple enzymes, (2) concerted inhibition, (3) cooperative feedback inhibition, and (4) cumulative feedback inhibition.

The multiple enzyme mechanism provides two or more enzymes for the initial step in the biosynthetic pathway. Each of the enzymes is sensitive to feedback inhibition by one of the products. If one product becomes heavily concentrated, it inhibits one of the enzymes, thus decreasing the output of the pathway, but still allowing some intermediate product to form and maintain the flow of reactants to the second product. If both products in a branched pathway become excessive, then both initial enzymes are inhibited and the productivity of the pathway is decreased. In concerted feedback inhibition, all of the end products must be present in excessive amounts to inhibit the common first step. Cooperative feedback inhibition provides partial suppression of the first step by each product. However, the joint effect of two or more products is greater than the sum of their individual partial effects. In cumulative feedback inhibition, each of the products at saturating concentration partially inhibits the common first step. When two or more products are at saturating concentrations, the suppressive effects are equivalent to the product of the individual concentration effects.

Regulation of Phosphorylase Activity. A concrete example of allosteric enzyme regulation is that of phosphorylase. Phosphorylase is an enzyme found in plant and animal tissues. It is particularly abundant in liver and muscle where it catalyzes the hydrolysis of glycogen in the presence of inorganic phosphate to produce glucose-1-phosphate. The glucose molecules are cleaved one at a time from the non-reducing end of the glycogen molecule. The control of phosphorylase activity is of obvious importance since glucose is used as a source of energy in respiration. Excessive amounts of glucose, however, can be deleterious because of toxic metabolic products. Mobilization of glucose for peak energy demand, such as physical exertion, must be counterbalanced by conservation of glucose during periods of rest. The control of phosphorylase activity is a complex process of feedback control involving several mechanisms. To fully appreciate the information flow and feedback regulation of the enzyme activity, we need to describe the molecular structure of the enzyme.

Phosphorylase is a complex molecule containing four subunits. Each protein subunit has a molecular weight of 125,000. When the subunits are separated from one another they are not active. Two subunits can unite to form a dimer with molecular weight of 250,000. The dimer is called phosphorylase b. It also is inactive unless large amounts of adenosive monophosphate (AMP) are present. AMP is an activator for phosphorylase b and upon binding to the effector site, the enzyme is fully active. This is clearly understandable in relation to information theory. AMP is a product of ATP breakdown. Therefore when the cell has used up much of its ATP in energy-requiring activities, large quantities of AMP are produced. In order to restore the ATP pool, glucose is needed to funnel into the respiration process where ATP is produced. AMP acts as a positive feedback signal to activate phosphorylase and thereby generate glucose for ATP production. When the excess AMP has been converted to ATP, the phosphorylase b molecule is no longer active. Two molecules of phosphorylase b combine in the presence of ATP, Mg^{2+}, and a kinase to form phosphorylase a—a tetramer with molecular weight of 500,000. Phosphorylase a is fully active and is formed by addition of a phosphate from ATP to each of the four subunits in the two phosphorylase b molecules. The enzyme catalyzing the phosphate transfer is phosphorylase b kinase. Phosphorylase a is inactivated by a phosphatase which hydrolyzes the phosphate linkages and separates the two phosphorylase b molecules. Phosphorylase b kinase is activated by adrenalin—a hormone secreted to arouse an organism during danger to flee or to fight. It is reasonable that the release of this hormone would activate phosphorylase since glucose is clearly needed to supply energy to support physical activity. Thus even in the presence of a large ATP pool, phosphorylase activity can be facilitated by the transformation of phosphorylase b to phosphorylase a. The presence of these multiple feedback activating systems ensures that enough glucose is generated under conditions of ATP depletion or when the organism is aroused. Conversely, when there is little need for glucose, the enzyme is largely inactive.

Feedback Control of Cell Respiration. The large process of respiration is also controlled by feedback mechanisms. The uptake of sugar by the cell, and the conversion of glucose-6-phosphate to fructose-1,6-diphosphate are controlled by positive and negative feedback mechanisms.

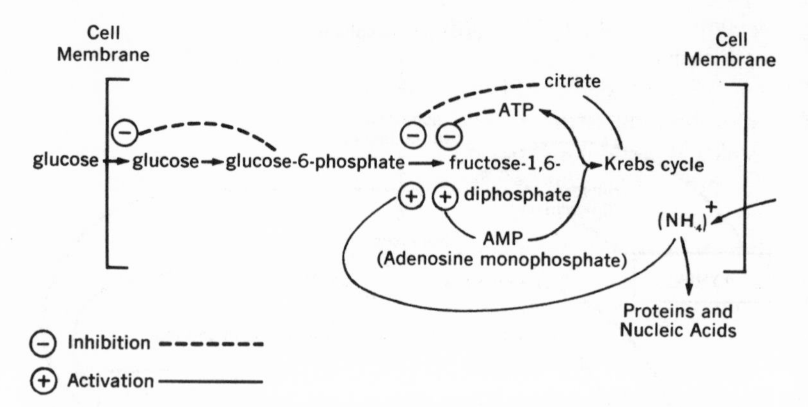

A saturation concentration of glucose-6-phosphate inhibits further glucose uptake across the membrane. A build up of glucose-6-phosphate indicates an inhibition of respiration. Therefore the cell no longer needs additional glucose. An abundance of citrate or ATP suppresses the conversion of glucose-6-phosphate to fructose-1,6-diphosphate. Abundance of citrate and ATP results when the cell has large reserve pools of energy rich molecules. Therefore, glycolysis need not proceed rapidly. However, excessive amounts of AMP or NH_4^+ activate the glycolysis pathway enzymes thereby yielding energy to convert the AMP to ATP and the production of Krebs cycle intermediates to be united with NH_4^+ in the synthesis of amino acids and nucleic acids. The biosynthesis of amino acids is under feedback control. When there are many branching pathways, there are several feedback mechanisms such that only the branch leading to a product is inhibited by the product.

Control mechanisms are also found at the tissue and organ levels. One of the most widely recognized unidirectional information flow mechanisms is that of plant growth hormones. The hormones are produced in the apical meristems of green plants. They move down the stem and they suppress lateral bud formation. The growth hormones are photosensitive and so pass down only the dark side of the stem, causing cell elongation as they move. There is uncertainty in the literature as to how the distribution of the growth hormone is regulated. The hormone may be

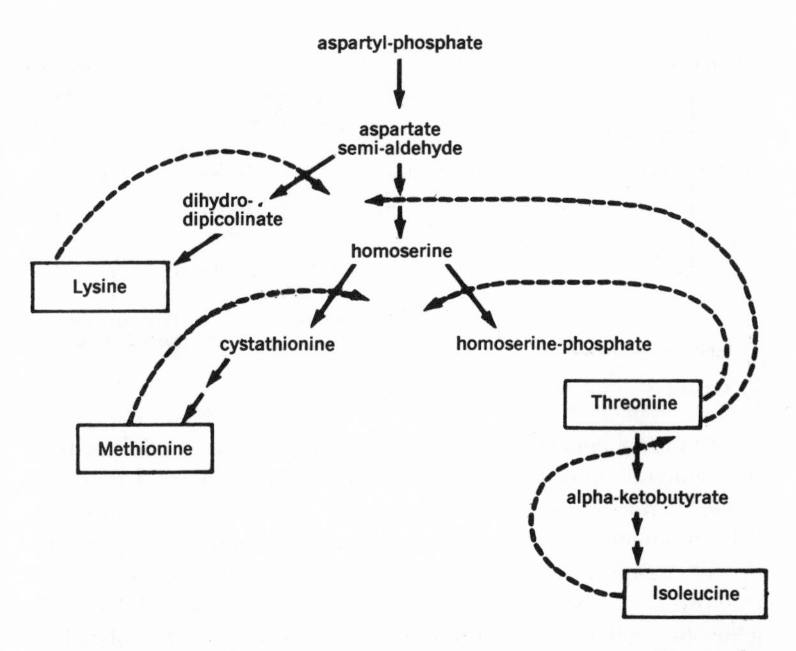

photolabile and thus destroyed on the side of the apex facing the light. Alternatively, it has been suggested that the hormone migrates to the dark side of the stem. In either case, the net result is that more hormone accumulates on the dark side of a stem than on the illuminated side. Consequently the dark side elongates more rapidly than the illuminated side and the plant bends toward the light source. This is a unidirectional information flow since there is no evidence that the elongating cells send a feedback signal to the apex in response to the hormone flow. The regulation of hormone concentration in the stem is more a function of external factors such as illumination than of internal factors.

Auxin Molecular Structure. It is not known precisely how the hormones regulate cell elongation. However, it is known that the chemical structure of the compounds determines their biological activity. One of the earliest discovered growth hormones was a class of messenger molecules called auxins. Knowledge of auxin molecular structure is essential to a full appreciation of their function. One of the earliest discovered auxins was beta-indoleacetic acid (IAA).

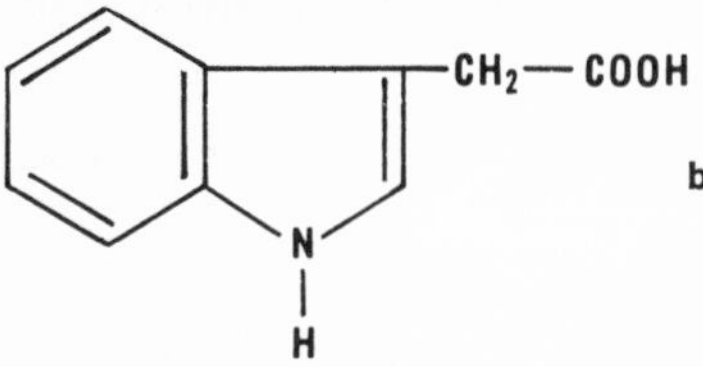

$-CH_2—COOH$

N

H

beta-indoleacetic acid

Several insightful studies on the relationship of auxin molecular structure to biological activity have shown that certain structural requirements must be met for a molecule to be active as a plant growth regulator. The molecule must contain: (1) an unsaturated ring (such as benzene or indole); (2) an organic acid side chain; and (3) a carboxyl group separated from the ring by other atomic groups (There are exceptions.). Inspection of the IAA molecular structure shows that it satisfies all of these requirements. It contains an unsaturated ring (a ring with double bonds), an organic acid side chain, and a carboxyl group separated from the ring by a methylene group ($-CH_2-$). Other biologically active compounds are indole-3-propionic acid and beta-naphthaleneacetic acid.

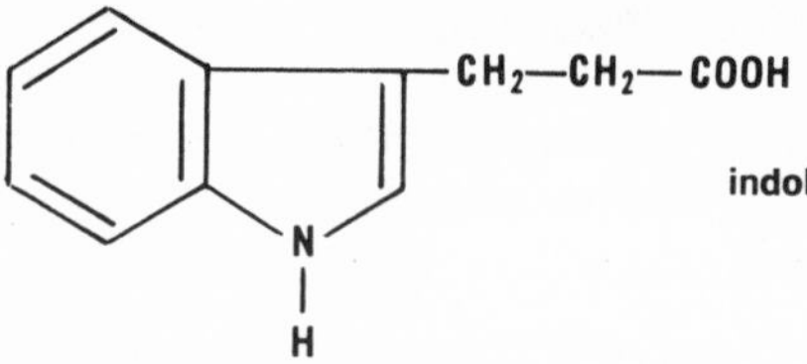

$-CH_2—CH_2—COOH$

N

H

indole-3-propionic acid

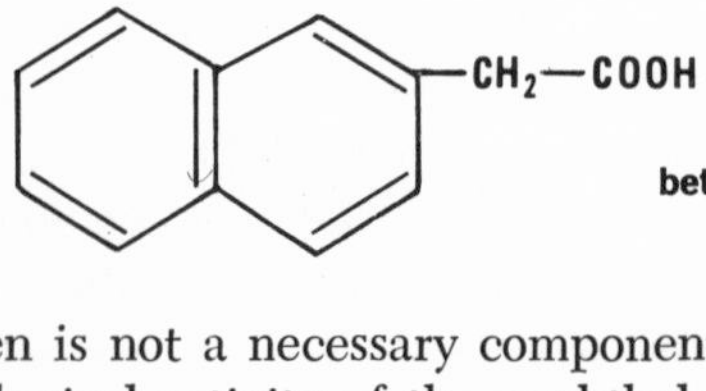

$-CH_2—COOH$

beta-naphthaleneacetic acid

Nitrogen is not a necessary component of the ring as shown by the biological activity of the naphthalene compounds. Alteration of the acid side chain destroys the messenger function of the molecule. Hydroxyl substitution in the side chain can destroy the biological activity of an otherwise fully active molecule. Thus, phenylacetic acid is active whereas alpha-hydroxyphenylacetic acid is not.

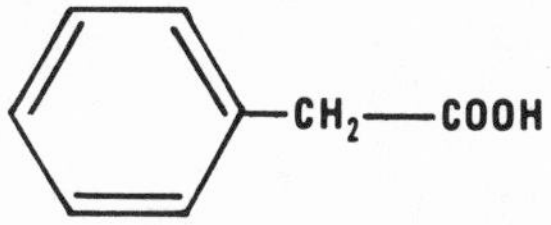

phenylacetic acid 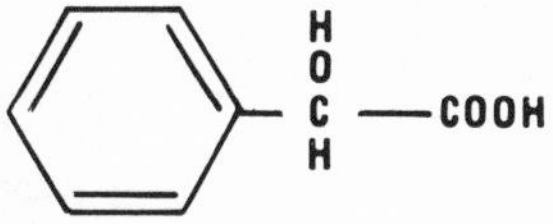 **alpha-hydroxyphenylacetic acid**

Substitution of a methyl group instead of a hydroxyl group does not interdict biological activity. Although most auxins have a carboxyl group separated from the ring, many exceptions to this rule have been found. For example, 2,3,6-trichlorobenzoic acid exhibits strong auxin activity.

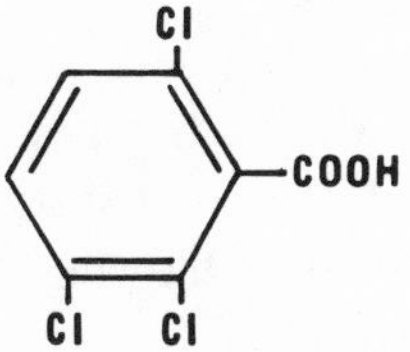

2,3,6-trichlorobenzoic acid

Auxin activity has been demonstrated in a wide variety of flowering plants among both the dicots and monocots.

Information Flow and Feedback Processes in Plants and Animals. Clear evidence is available from the earliest studies on auxin activity that these messenger molecules are activated in the stem apex and that these tissues are the source of auxin flow to the lower parts of the stem. Charles Darwin was among the first biologists to suggest that plant growth might be regulated by substances produced at the tips of stems. Darwin concluded that bending of seedlings toward a light source was due to some influence transmitted from the upper part to the lower part of the stem. The rather speculative explanations of plant stem curvature developed by Darwin were confirmed in the early 1900's in decisive experiments performed by Boysen-Jensen, Paal, and Went. Boysen-Jensen demonstrated that the regulatory influence described by Darwin was a material substance and not some intangible influence such as biological electricity. Thus, Boysen-Jensen clearly established the presence of information molecules in the plant stem. He began with the assumption that some regulatory effect originated in the stem apex. To determine whether the regulator was a material substance, he made a transverse cut just beneath the apex of an oat coleoptile on the side *opposite to* a light source. A sheet of mica was inserted in the cut. The oat coleoptile did not bend toward the light source. Insertion of mica in a slit on the illuminated side of a coleoptile did not inhibit bending toward the light source. These clever but simple experiments showed that a material substance was being produced in the stem apex and that its migration down the dark side of a stem enhanced the stem's bending toward a light source.

Paal further confirmed the material quality of the growth regulator. He decapitated coleoptiles by removing their tips and placed the plants in a dark chamber. A small segment of each tip was replaced on one half of the transected coleoptile surface. Thus, if any substance were diffusing from the tip into the coleoptile, it would move down only that side and cause that side to elongate. As a result, the whole coleoptile would bend. Frits Went demonstrated that the messenger molecules were isolatable. He placed coleoptile tips on small blocks of agar which absorbed material secreted by the tips. The agar blocks were placed laterally on a transected coleoptile tip and bending was induced away from the side where the agar had been placed. The degree of curvature was proportional to the amount of active substance absorbed by the agar. The many experiments of Went and his carefully quantified results clearly established the presence of messenger molecules in plant stems and placed the explanation. of plant phototropism on a firm empirical foundation.

Messenger molecules in the form of hormones are also widely represented in the animal kingdom. Growth, reproduction cycles, arousal to action, and metabolic rate are examples of animal functions regulated by information-carrying molecules produced in one organ and distributed to target organs where activity is altered. Blood pressure regulation in mammals is clearly an example of feedback control. Nervous system receptors detect changes in blood pressure. The receptors located in arteries and in the heart send signals to the medulla where central nervous system mechanisms are activated to send efferent impulses to the heart and vessels. Changes in cardiac rate and vasomotor dilation compensate for blood pressure changes. A drop in blood pressure produces increased cardiac rate and blood vessel constriction thus increasing systemic blood pressure. Conversely, a rise in blood pressure results in nervous impulses producing reduced cardiac rate and increasing blood vessel dilation thus reducing blood pressure. An obvious value of information theory in biological research is its capacity to integrate and explain a wide variety of biological phenomena at all levels of biological organization in both plants and animals.

Analysis of Lesson Six

The lesson is organized around the central theme of information and control in biological systems. The major objective of the lesson is to communicate information about trends and sequences such as the process of feedback mechanisms in biosynthetic pathways and the regulation of growth in plant tissue. General principles of enzyme activity and growth hormone action are presented. The lesson as a whole illustrates the use of a general principle of feedback regulation as an explanation of diverse biological processes at the cellular, tissue, and organismic levels. A serial-centered organization is used throughout most of the lesson. Most of the topics are presented in a sequence as isolated units of information without an effort to make multiple comparisons or interrelationships among the various ideas.

The sequential organization of the lesson with reference to the eight cell model is fairly complex. The lesson moves through six phases. They are represented in the eight cell model by the following sequence of cells: 4, 2, 6, 2, 7, and 2. The lesson begins with a general discussion of feedback control mechanisms. The variations in occurrence of the mechanisms are discussed (cell 4).

A section of the lesson is devoted to a discussion of general mechanisms of enzyme feedback control. This segment of the lesson is classified as a presentation of general processes of a constant kind (cell 2). A concrete example of feedback control and information flow is given in the example of phosphorylase inhibition and activation. This is a specific process of a constant kind (cell 6). A general discussion of respiration follows which is classified in cell 2. Then, specific molecular structures of auxins are cited and variations in structure are described as related to the biological activity of the molecule. This discussion of variability in activity as a function of molecular structure indicates a classification in cell 7. The final section of the lesson is devoted to a description of general feedback processes and information flow in plants and animals with emphasis on the organismic level. The content is classified in cell 2. I recognize that this section is difficult to classify since the particular examples of feedback control and information flow presented are rather concrete. However, they are general processes occurring in a wide variety of mammals and higher plants and therefore appear to be best classified as generalities.

Lesson Seven Irritability and Activity

The survival of an organism in an environmental niche depends in large measure on its capacity to sense stimuli and make appropriate responses toward a better adjustment to the environment. Sensitivity to environmental stimuli is called irritability. Activity is a response of an organism to internal or external stimuli. Activity can manifest itself as internal changes in organ function such as changes in cardiac rate, respiratory rate, secretory activity, and blood vessel dilation and constriction. Usually we think of activity as an external manifestation, such as changes in posture, movement of appendages, and locomotion. In the more general sense, activity is any adjustment in behavior (internal or external) produced by sensory stimulation (Berrill; Katz). Among all living things, animals have clearly developed the most elaborate sensory and responding mechanisms. Animals are remarkably and elegantly adapted to make rapid and efficient responses to environmental stimulation. A few plants have developed specialized structures that permit rapid responding to environmental events. The carnivorous plant venus flytrap (*Dionea muscipula*) has hinged leaves bearing sensitive hairs on their inner surfaces. When an unwary insect contacts the hairs several times, the leaves close abruptly trapping the insect. Digestion of the trapped prey probably yields some nutrients for the plant thereby favoring its survival. The sundew (*Drosera rotundifolia*) has sticky hairs on the surface of its leaves which snare and gradually enclose insects attracted to its surface. Aside from the carnivorous plants, some legumes are sensitive to touch. The compound leaves of the sensitive plant (*Mimosa pudica*) collapse when touched. These changes are believed to be produced by alterations in hydrostatic pressure in the leaf cells, particularly in the supporting cells in the pulvinus at the base of the leaf petiole. Among lower plants, some motile algae are particularly responsive to light and swim rapidly toward sources of moderate illumination. Such rapid responses to environmental stimuli are not common among the higher plants. Most advanced plants make slow responses to environmental changes and these are seldom in the form of rapid gross movements. Light, temperature, moisture, and mineral salts are stimuli arousing plant responses. Changes in day length, day and night temperature, or quality of light may induce changes in growth or flowering time, but these responses develop over several days or weeks and are mediated by changes in hormone activity. The higher plants have no specialized tissue or organ systems to receive and respond to environmental stimuli. The stem apex of most higher plants is the source of a growth hormone which regulates bending of the stem toward a light source. However, this is clearly not the only function of the apex. It contains a mass of meristematic tissue which produces new tissue and organs during plant development.

Nervous System Structure. By contrast, most animals, and particularly the higher animals, have developed a specialized sensory and responding system to allow rapid adjustment to environmental stimuli. The animal nervous system is clearly specialized to receive external and internal stimuli, to integrate the sensory input, and to produce changes in behavior. The nervous system consists of three basic components: (1) receptors to sense stimuli, (2) an afferent nerve path to carry incoming nerve signals to centers of integration, and (3) an efferent nerve path to direct impulses to effector organs. The effector organs can be muscles to produce motion or glands that release substances vital to the life of the organism. Receptors are classified according to the stimuli to which they are most sensitive. Photoreceptors receive light stimulation, mechanoreceptors sense touch and pressure, and chemoreceptors are sensitive to chemicals. The afferent and efferent nerve paths are chains of nerve cells. Each nerve cell makes surface contact with its neighbor in the chain. Thus, although there is no cytoplasmic continuity between cells, nerve impulses are transmitted across the point of contact between two nerve cells. A nerve cell is called a neuron. It consists of a mass of cytoplasm with nucleus, mitochondria, and other organelles typical of most mammalian cells. The morphology of the neuron reflects its specialized function of signal conduction. The main body, or perikaryon, of the neuron is a mass of cytoplasm containing the nucleus. On one side of the perikaryon, radiating outward from its surface, there are short branched protrusions called dendrites which receive incoming nerve impulses. On the opposite side of the neuron is a much longer extension called the axon which transmits nerve impulses to the next neuron in sequence. The axon terminates as a system of fine branching nerve endings.

Nervous System Activity. The nerve impulse carried by a neuron is an electrical signal. Considerable information is available on the physiological origin of the nerve impulse and the mechanism for its conduction. Nerve impulses originate on the surface membrane of a neuron. There is an electrical potential difference between the outside and inside surface of a neuron membrane. The outside surface carries positive charges and the inside surface bears negative charges. The difference in electrical potential arises from an excess of sodium ions on the outside of the membrane as compared to the inside. Sodium ions (Na^+) are continuously pumped outside of the cell through active transport—

a process supported by metabolic release of energy. The negative internal charge is produced by an excess of organic acids and other anions. Although sodium is largely concentrated on the outside of the cell membrane, potassium ions are concentrated on the inside of the membrane. The differential distribution of positive and negative ions across the nerve membrane produces a voltage of approximately 50 millivolts. At this point we should recognize that most living cells have a potential difference across their surface membranes. The nerve cell, however, has become highly specialized to use this source of energy as a mechanism for impulse transmission. The membrane potential of an unexcited nerve cell is called the resting potential. It can be measured by inserting a fine electrode into the nerve and placing a reference electrode on the surface. These measurements give readings of approximately 50 to 60 millivolts for a variety of nerve cells.

When a nerve is stimulated by physical contact or by electrical stimulation, a local change in permeability of the membrane occurs. Sodium ions diffuse rapidly into the cell. The potential difference across the membrane is momentarily abolished and the outside of the membrane at the point of stimulation becomes negatively charged. This flow of ions and the consequent change in surface potential produces a local electrical impulse called an action potential. During the inward flow of sodium ions, the outside surface of the nerve membrane can become 100 or more millivolts negative relative to the inner surface. After the sodium ions have diffused inside the cell, potassium ions diffuse out to balance the charge distribution. The action potential amplitude gradually decays as the potassium ion concentration builds up and abolishes the negative surface charge. The local impulse lasts about 1.0 millisecond. Eventually the sodium and potassium ions are redistributed with sodium on the outside and potassium on the inside. During the period of the action potential, and for sometime thereafter, the nerve is insensitive to further stimulation near the site of the action potential. This is called the absolutely refractory period. Its duration varies among different kinds of nerve cells, but is approximately 0.4 to 0.7 milliseconds. The absolutely refractory period is followed by one of less intensity called the relatively refractory period. During this period of time, the cell can be stimulated but the stimulus must be stronger than normally required. The cell is said to have an elevated excitatory threshold. The threshold stimulus is one just sufficiently intense to arouse an action potential. Neurons obey an *all or none law* of excitation. The stimulus applied must be sufficiently intense to evoke a reaction. If the stimulus is below threshold, no response occurs. If the stimulus is at or above threshold, the full action potential is aroused. The nerve cell does not make a graded response to variations in stimulus intensity. The stimulus either evokes the full scale action potential (all) or none at all (none).

If the arousal of an action potential were only a local phenomenon on the surface of the nerve cell, there would be little communication advantage to it. However, the arousal of an action potential produces a wave of excitation along the nerve cell. Each point of depolarization causes local electrical currents which produce depolarization of an adjacent part of the membrane and thus a series of action potentials are propagated along the nerve cell surface. Some neurophysiologists compare it to the action of a fuse. Each point of ignition in a fuse releases heat energy which ignites the next part and so the train of ignition is maintained throughout the length of the fuse. Of course, in the nerve cell the excitatory stimulus which sustains the series of impulses is an electrical stimulus, not a heat stimulus. When an action potential is evoked, the outer surface of the membrane becomes locally negatively charged. This sets up external currents as positive ions flow from adjacent areas to the negative site. The inside of the membrane becomes positively charged at the site of the action potential and internal currents are also induced as negative ions flow from nearby surfaces to the positive sites. The net result of the local internal and external current flow is to cause depolarization of the membrane surface nearest to the site of the action potential. This results in an arousal of an action potential at the adjacent site and so the process proceeds along the entire length of the nerve cell. This is illustrated as steps A through D in the diagram. The action potential is represented by a unimodal peak at each point of depolarization. At step A, the cell is in a resting

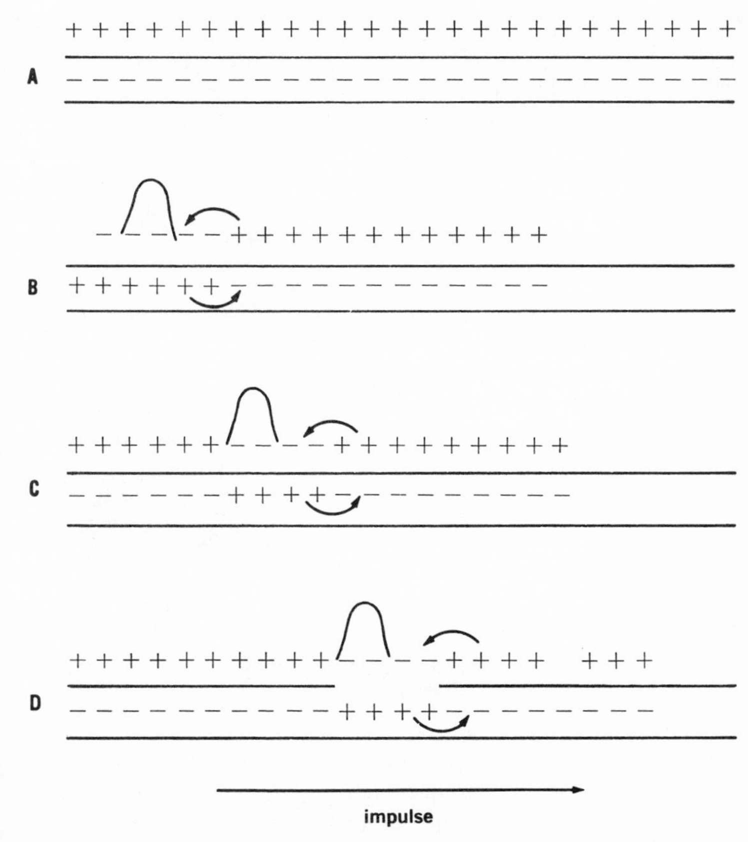

stage. At step B, the first action potential is evoked which then sets up a train of impulses.

Progress of the series of action potentials can be followed by attaching electrodes to the nerve at two different points and connecting them to a sensitive galvanometer or an oscilloscope. This allows us to follow the flow of current between the two points on the nerve surface. When a nerve is stimulated at a point distant to the electrodes, the passage of the impulse along the nerve produces a diphasic curve in the galvanometric record. The curve has two peaks, one above the abscissa and one below.

The first peak is produced when the impulse reaches the first electrode. The current flows from the second electrode to the depolarized site of the first electrode where the surface of the membrane has become negative from loss of sodium ions. As

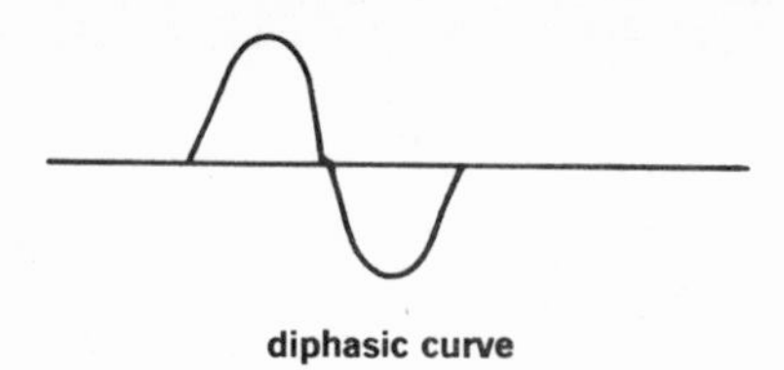

diphasic curve

the impulse moves away from the first electrode site toward the second one, the first electrode site repolarizes. Eventually, the second electrode site depolarizes as the impulse moves toward it. The second electrode becomes negative and the current flow reverses through the galvanometer thus causing the downward directed curve in the graph. If the nerve is injured by crushing a segment between the two electrodes, only a monophasic curve is produced. The second electrode site does not become depolarized since the nerve impulse is blocked at the crushed site. Nerve impulse transmission can also be blocked by applying a strong anodal current to the nerve. The localized increase in positive charge prevents depolarization of the membrane at that site and the propagation of the impulse is stopped. Examination of nerve tissue with the electron microscope has shown that the axon is surrounded by a multilayered set of membranes called a myelin sheath. The sheath is produced by a nearby cell called a Schwann cell. The Schwann cell produces a thin membranous lip which wraps around the axon in a spiral fashion producing a multilayered coating. At certain points along the axon, the myelin membrane is incomplete and produces a depressed node exposing the axon membrane. These nodal areas are called the Nodes of Ranvier. The myelin sheath acts as an insulator around the axon very much as the rubber coating around an electrical wire insulates it from the environment.

Until recently it was not understood how the nerve impulse travels along the myelinated axon. It has become clearly established, however, that the Nodes of Ranvier are the sites at which

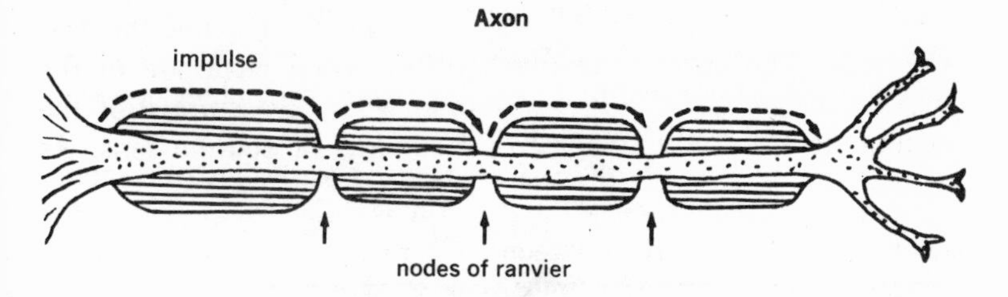

impulse propagation takes place. In a non-myelinated nerve, the action potential is propagated as explained earlier by a stepwise depolarization of the membrane surface. The impulse conduction rate is determined by the velocity of excitation of each site along the nerve. In a non-myelinated nerve, the impulse is propagated by many small-step depolarizations. In a myelinated nerve, the rate of conduction is increased since the excitation jumps from one node to the next.

This leap-frog pattern of impulse propagation is called saltatory conduction. Nerve impulses are carried along nerve fibers composed of many neurons in serial association, the axon of one neuron ending upon the dendrites of another. The axon may terminate on other parts of the adjacent neuron body when an inhibitory action is to be produced. Generally when an impulse is to be transmitted without decrement, the axon endings are in contact with the membrane of the dendrites. Most neurons conduct impulses in only one direction, namely from the dendrites toward the axon. A question that remains to be answered is how does the impulse get transmitted from axon to dendrite? We know that the axon does not make direct cytoplasmic contact with the dendrite of the second neuron. Electron microscopic

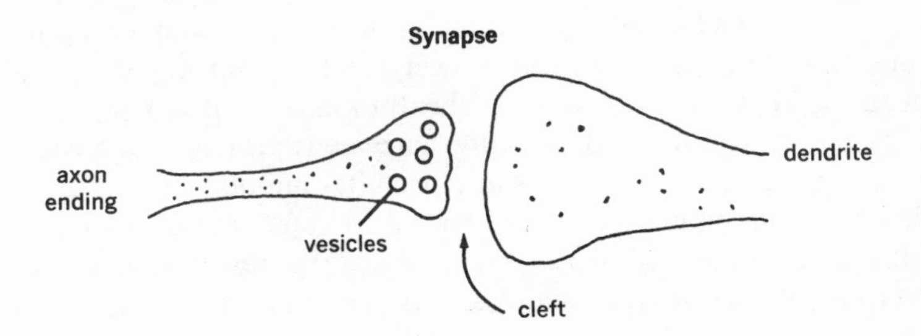

examination of the association between axon and dendrite reveals that the two membrane surfaces are separated by a narrow channel called the synaptic cleft. The region of contact between an axon and dendrite is called the synapse.

The membrane of the axon is called the presynaptic membrane and the membrane of the dendrite is called the postsynaptic membrane. The cleft between the two membranes is very narrow, being about 120 angstroms in width.

There are two hypotheses about the mechanism of synaptic transmission of impulses: the electrical and the chemical. The electrical hypothesis assumes that the depolarization of the axon membrane sets up local electrical currents which cause a depolarization of the opposite dendrite membrane. This is a conservative hypothesis since it presumes the same excitatory mechanisms occur in synaptic transmission of impulses as occur along the nerve fiber. If this were true, the rate of synaptic transmission should be very rapid. In some cases however, the synaptic transmission delay is 0.3 to 10 milliseconds. The presynaptic membrane potential has already decayed before the postsynaptic potential appears. These observations suggest that an alternative mechanism must exist.

The chemical hypothesis assumes that a transmitter substance is present in the axon ending. When the impulse arrives at the presynaptic membrane of the axon, the transmitter substance is released into the synaptic cleft. It diffuses across the cleft and evokes an action potential in the postsynaptic membrane. The time required for diffusion of the transmitter substance across the cleft could account for the 0.3 to 10 millisecond delay. It has been suggested that the transmitter substance may be acetylcholine. Histochemical studies have shown that the enzyme acetylcholine esterase is localized at certain synaptic junctions. This enzyme cleaves acetylcholine into choline and acetic acid. If acetylcholine is the transmitter substance, it is logical to expect that a degradative enzyme is present in the cleft to destroy excess transmitter substance after impulse transmission has been accomplished. Electron microscopic examination of ultra-thin sections of nerve tissue shows the existence of numerous vesicles in the cytoplasm of the axon. These may be acetylcholine-containing vesicles which empty their contents into the synaptic cleft when the nerve impulse arrives at the axon ending.

The neuromuscular junction is a synapse. Physiological study of this synapse yields strong evidence in support of the chemical transmission hypothesis. Muscular contraction is regulated by impulses from efferent nerves which send axon nerve endings onto the muscle surface. The point of contact between the axon ending and the muscle surface is called a motor end-plate. The axon ending makes contact with the muscle cell membrane, but as with interneuronal synapses there is no cytoplasmic connection between the nerve ending and the muscle cell. When a nerve impulse reaches the axon nerve endings on the muscle, acetylcholine is released and the muscle fiber is stimulated to contract. Evidence in support of the chemical transmission mechanism for neuro-motor stimulation is the following. Poisoning acetylcholine esterase, thereby preventing destruction of the transmitter substance in the cleft, results in multiple contractions of the muscle when a nerve impulse is generated in the motor axon innervating the muscle. This is expected since the residual acetylcholine excites the muscle after each contraction, thus setting up a series of spasms. When electrical potential changes of either polarity are imposed on the axon ending of a motor end plate, they do not spread beyond the nerve ending to the muscle, but they do increase acetylcholine discharge. Application of acetylcholine directly to the muscle membrane of the motor end plate produces a membrane depolarization and contraction of the muscle. The mechanism of acetylecholine-induced muscle membrane depolarization is not fully understood, but it is hypothesized that the acetylcholine causes an increase in membrane permeability thus initiating sodium and potassium exchange across the membrane. An action potential is initiated in the muscle membrane producing a wave of contraction.

We have discussed the message-carrying capacity of efferent nerves and the muscle action they arouse. The afferent nervous system also carries nerve signals as a series of nerve impulses. Afferent nerve fibers are activated by changes in receptor membrane potential aroused by sensory stimulation. Intense stimulation evokes a high frequency discharge in the afferent nerve pathway, whereas a mild stimulus produces a train of low frequency impulses. The signal carried by the afferent nerves is transmitted to the efferent nerves through the spinal cord or ascends into higher brain centers where various selection and association mechanisms direct the impulse to the efferent nerve pathways. We can now link the concepts of irritability and activity to one another. We shall use the example of a simple reflex arc to illustrate the relationship between the two biological functions.

Reflex Arc. A reflex arc is a connection between afferent and efferent nerves at the level of the spinal cord. The reflex arc is a very efficient mechanism for rapid responding to noxious or harmful stimuli. Consider the case of rapid finger withdrawal on burning in a flame. The pain receptors arouse a high frequency impulse train in the afferent nerves, innervating the burned finger. The impulse is transmitted directly to the efferent nervous system across a synapse in the spinal cord. The high frequency afferent impulse arouses a high frequency signal in many of the efferent nerve fibers supplying the muscles in the arm of the injured finger. The arrival of the impulses at the muscle evokes a massive contraction of the muscle fibers, thus causing withdrawal of the injured finger. Activity follows almost immediately upon irritation since there is no mediation by the higher brain centers. Of course, afferent stimulation also passes upward through the spinal cord to various higher brain centers, thus arousing awareness at the conscious level of the nature and location of the stimulation. However, the reflex arc permits rapid withdrawal of the affected part before the slower cognitive (mental) processes intervene. The rapid adjustment of an animal to potentially destructive stimuli through reflex action favors its survival since it can more efficiently withdraw from harmful stimuli than an organism without such specialization of function.

Higher mental activity in response to irritation is of obvious value. An organism that can behave flexibly and make new associative responses to previously encountered stimuli is more likely to avoid danger, find food and secure it more efficiently, and discover new habitats more effectively than organisms which do not have the capacity to modulate and select activity in relation to irritation. The development of the brain during evolution and the concurrent capacity to respond divergently to environmental stimulation has greatly enhanced the survival and success of animals in the terrestrial environment. The almost explosive evolution of animals in the terrestrial environment was no doubt enhanced by their capacity to efficiently and flexibly coordinate activity with sensory stimulation. The success of man in adapting to and controlling the environment for his greater survival is largely a product of the sophistication of his nervous system. Clearly the principle of irritability and activity is a central concept in understanding organismic adaptation to the environment and enhanced survival within an environmental niche.

Analysis of Lesson Seven

This lesson illustrates communication of neurophysiological data within the context of the general theme of irritability and activity. The major objective is to communicate information about processes of nerve conduction and control of muscular activity. This is a reception lesson with knowledge acquisition as its basic outcome objective.

The first part of the lesson is serial-centered with a discussion of the various components of the nervous system being presented in sequential order. The last part of the lesson on the reflex arc mechanism (page 188) is cluster-centered. Here, the various mechanisms of nervous system activity are interrelated and the concepts of irritability and activity are linked to one another.

The sequential organization of the lesson with reference to the eight cell model proceeds through four steps. The introduction to the lesson contains a general discussion of various sensory mechanisms occurring in plants and animals. The variations in kinds of sensory mechanisms in plants are discussed and the general organization of animal nervous systems is presented. Since the discussion contains citations of variations in sensory processes at a general level, the content is classified as cell 4. Thereafter, the structure of the nervous system is discussed at a fairly general level (not specific to any one organism). This is classified as cell 1. The process of nerve conduction is discussed under the heading of *nervous system activity*. This is a general discussion of nerve impulse propogation (cell 2). The lesson concludes with a general discussion of the integration of irritability and activity as illustrated by a reflex arc. The processes of nerve conduction and muscular contraction are discussed at a rather general level (cell 2). This lesson is in large measure a general discussion of nervous system structure and function. It contains few specifics with the exception of the illustrations of plant sensitivity given in the introduction. These, however, are embedded within a larger context of a general discussion of plant and animal irritability. If the lesson had given extended attention to the structure and activity of specific nerve cells such as the squid giant axon or Mauthner's cells in fishes, this would have constituted a discussion of specifics and would have warranted classifying the content in one of the cells on specifics (cells 5 through 8).

Lesson Eight Aquatic Life: Interaction among Living Things

The complexity and rich variety of life processes are everywhere evident at all levels of biological organization. Living things are dependent upon one another for food, protection, and maintenance of a favorable environment (Dowdeswell; Kormondy; Macan). Aquatic plants provide food and protection for small animals that live among them. The production of oxygen by plants supports animal respiration. In turn, animals expire carbon dioxide used by plants in photosynthesis. Plants trap light energy and use mineral matter dissolved from the surrounding soil and rocks to produce food ingested by animals. This complex network of associations among living things and with their environment is dynamically illustrated in aquatic communities. Here dwell a myriad of plants and animals, some clearly visible to the naked eye and others so small that they can be seen only with the aid of high power microscopes. Some dwell at the surface of the water, others live at various intermediate depths

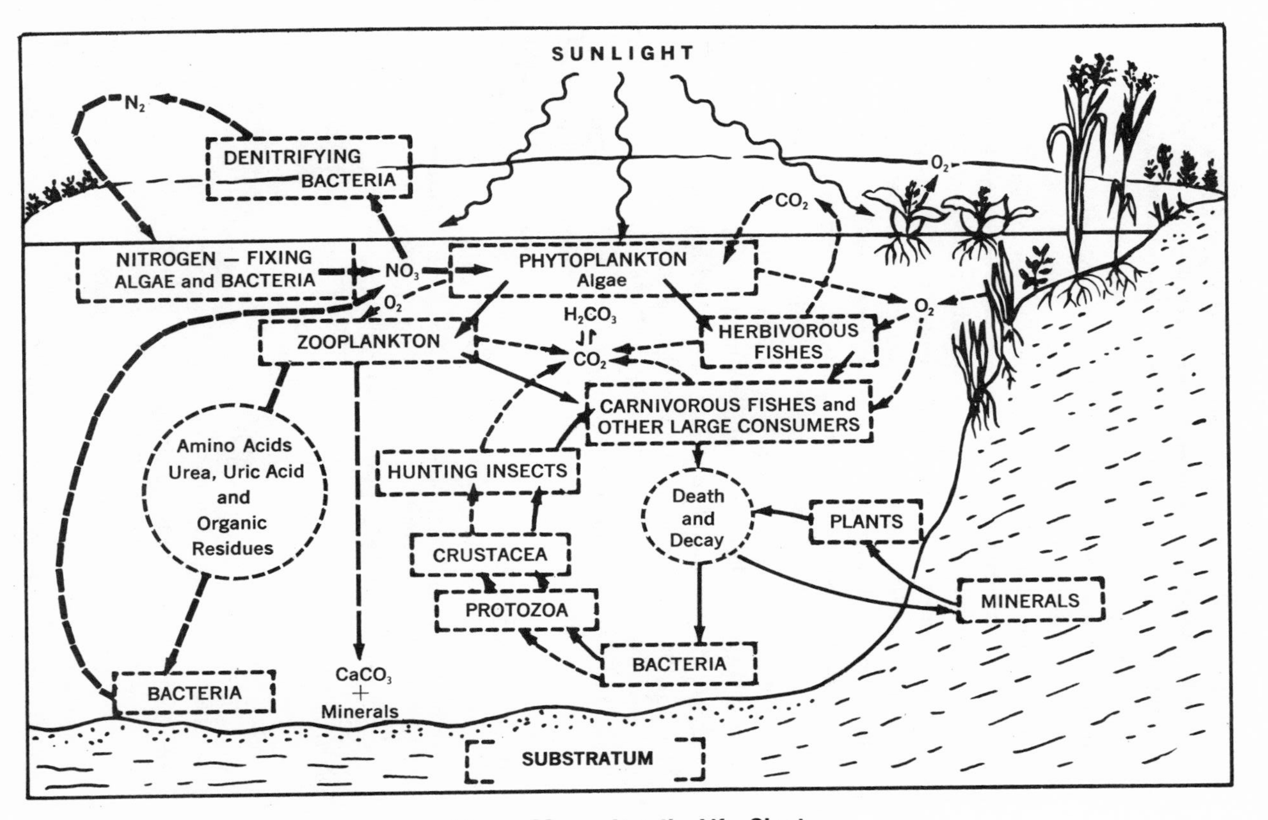

Figure 22 Aquatic Life Chart

and some plumb the very bottom depths where they live within the surface layers of mud and debris. On an early summer day, a pond may appear to be a very placid environment. However, superficial appearances can be deceiving—beneath its placid surface there exists a world of activity, teeming at both the chemical and biological levels.

Figure 22 illustrates some of the many activities that accompany and sustain life in the water. Once one understands these many processes, the observation of a pond clearly becomes a more rich and remarkable experience. Even a simple system such as a well-stocked aquarium has greater meaning for one who understands the richness of the chemical and living processes that combine to support life there. The figure illustrates the interaction among three major factors of life in aquatic communities: the 1) geological, 2) chemical, and 3) biological factors. The geological factors include the kind of substratum underlying the pond and the composition of rocks and soil that surround a pond and cover its bottom surfaces. The turbidity of the water is one factor determining the amount and quality of light penetrating beneath the surface layers. Chemical factors include the amount and kind of minerals dissolved in the water and the availability of essential nutrients such as nitrogen, phosphorous, oxygen, and carbon dioxide. During several chemical cycles essential nutrients are regenerated after utilization by various aquatic organisms. Some chemical nutrients continuously undergo exchange between biological organisms and the non-living environment. Living things feed upon one another thereby establishing a close dependence among themselves for survival. The destruction of any one of the participants in the complex food network can threaten the existence of the whole aquatic system.

The arrows and boxes in the Aquatic Life Chart illustrate the complex interdependence of living and non-living factors in maintenance of an aquatic system. The geology of the rock and soil underlying a pond (substratum) influences the quality of the pond water. Large masses of calcareous rocks (calcium carbonate) make the water alkaline, whereas an abundance of soil and decaying organic matter produces an acidic environment. The pH of the water limits the kinds of plants that grow there and hence indirectly determines the kinds of animals that can be supported in the aquatic ecosystem. An ecosystem is an assemblage of living things in relation to their abiotic environment. An aquatic ecosystem comprises the physical environment of a body of water and the living things that inhabit that environment. Certain aquatic plants such as algae grow in a narrow pH range, and extremes of pH not only alter the quality of floating and rooted plants, but also alter the kinds that grow there. Soft water (neutral to mildly acidic pH) supports a rich growth of algae such as desmids, and certain species of blue-green, golden brown, and green algae. These do not flourish in hard water. Certain animals show a preference for calcium-rich water. The crayfish is such an organism; it thrives in calcium-rich water, and is seldom found in lime-free environments. The mineral composition of the underlying rock determines the inorganic nutrients available to living things in the pond. The edge of a pond supports luxuriant growth of rooted plants if there is sufficient soil to provide anchorage. A rich growth of swamp plants provides a hiding place for young fish and supports the growth of smaller organisms upon which they feed.

There are various chemical nutrient cycles which provide a constant supply of essential elements for the growth of living organisms. Nitrogen is an essential element for the synthesis of proteins, nucleic acids, and other macromolecules. Most nitrogen is available as a gas in the atmosphere. However, gaseous nitrogen is not readily assimilated by most organisms and must be oxidized to nitrate. As shown in the left-hand part of the Aquatic Life Chart, certain nitrogen-fixing organisms such as blue-green algae and bacteria produce nitrates from atmospheric nitrogen. The process of converting gaseous nitrogen to nitrate is called nitrogen fixation. Aquatic plants assimilate the nitrates to produce organic molecules. Small herbivores (plant-eating animals) consume the nitrogen-containing macromolecules to build up their own tissues. These organisms excrete nitrogen-containing compounds that are assimilated by bacteria, and when the organism dies it is decomposed by bacteria. Bacterial digestion of organic molecules releases nitrates into the water. Denitrifying bacteria, however, reduce some of the nitrates to gaseous nitrogen which can be released into the atmosphere. Thus, the nitrogen cycle is complete.

Carbon is also conserved in a biogeochemical cycle. Carbon dioxide produced by animal and plant respiration or by combustion and volcanic activity enters the atmosphere. Atmospheric carbon dioxide is absorbed by rain water and accumulates in ponds as carbonic acid (H_2CO_3) which readily dissociates to form free carbon dioxide gas, or bicarbonate and carbonate ions. Some carbon dioxide in pond water is produced by respiration of submerged plants and animals. Although animals are the main source of carbon dioxide production among living things, roots of plants, and green parts of plants during darkness, make carbon dioxide as a product of their respiration. Floating microscopic green plants (phytoplankton) absorb carbon dioxide during photosynthesis as shown in the Aquatic Life Chart and use it to produce sugars and other organic molecules. These organic molecules are consumed by predators such as the herbivorous fishes and zooplankton. During respiration, the carbon stored in these macromolecules is released as carbon dioxide. Thus the carbon cycle is completed.

Oxygen is also cycled in living processes. Green plants release oxygen by photolysis of water during photosynthesis. The released oxygen is utilized by animals during respiration to produce water and yield high energy compounds to maintain life. There are many other examples of nutrient cycles not shown in the Aquatic Life Chart. Phosphorous and sulfur each have separate biogeochemical cycles. Not all of the carbon and minerals assimilated by organisms are immediately recycled. As shown in the chart, some carbon is lost as calcium carbonate ($CaCO_3$) which precipitates as shells of dead organisms. These accumulate at the bottom of the pond and help contribute to the build up of the substratum. Some other minerals are also carried down in this manner.

The interactions among living things in an aquatic ecosystem forms a network of food chains. A food chain is a sequence of predator-prey relationships wherein larger organisms feed upon smaller ones. A food chain usually begins with a photosynthetic organism such as an alga that can utilize light energy to produce energy-rich organic molecules. Since these organisms trap energy from primary sources such as sunlight, they are called producers. These organisms produce the food molecules that are consumed by other organisms. Those predators which prey upon producers are called consumers. Most of the producers are phytoplankton—floating algae and small vascular plants. The small consumers are zooplankton—swimming forms of protozoa and crustacea. Herbivorous fishes also feed upon the floating plants. These consumers are in turn eaten by larger carnivorous (flesh-eating) organisms. Eventually, the large carnivores die and their flesh is decayed by bacteria. The bacteria serve as an origin of another food chain including protozoa, crustacea, hunting insects, and carnivorous fishes. This cycle of organic molecular utilization is shown in the lower middle part of the chart. The network of predator-prey relationships is called a food web. The complex intertwining of the various food chains suggest a web-like association—hence the name food web.

The Aquatic Life Chart amply illustrates the close dependence of living things upon the environment for sources of energy (sunlight), mineral nutrients, and suitable shelter. The remarkable economy of natural processes is illustrated by the several nutrient cycles. The complex interdependence of living things upon one another as sources of food is shown by the food web and the flow of carbon and oxygen between animals and plants. The entire aquatic ecosystem is dependent on the surrounding water mass as a medium for support and locomotion, and as carrier of food and mineral nutrients for maintenance of life. Of great importance is the remarkable thermal stability of water masses. Water tends to change temperature only gradually under extremes in fluctuation of atmospheric temperature. Many aquatic organisms are cold-blooded. Unlike mammals, they cannot regulate their body temperature and therefore are dependent on the surrounding water mass to maintain suitable temperatures for life. The efficient thermal stability of water masses helps to support the life of these countless organisms. The rich supply of oxygen in flowing water, and in standing water with large surface area, provides an ideal environment for respiring organisms. The interdependence of living things among themselves and upon the abiotic environment is indeed a complex and delicate balance of interactions. We can conclude that the surrounding water mass is truly the matrix of life supporting the diverse interactions among aquatic organisms and with their environment.

Analysis of Lesson Eight

This sample lesson on aquatic life simulates a communication based on a theme of interactions among living things. The Aquatic Life Chart provides a figural summary of the various interactions to be discussed, and hence serves as a theme giving continuity to the verbal communication. This is an example of the use of a figural model as a theme for a lesson. The objective of the lesson is to communicate knowledge of specific facts about aquatic organisms, processes of nutrient exchange, and principles of organization in ecosystems. The presentation is a short, general discussion of aquatic ecosystems. A much longer lesson could be developed around the theme of interactions in aquatic ecosystems by giving additional details on the contribution of rock weathering to aquatic mineral content, the various kinds of organisms that occupy the several niches in the chart, and the role of competition among organisms in an ecosystem.

The lesson is largely serial-centered. Each major concept is considered in sequential order, with most of its multiple relationships omitted. At certain points are brief cluster-centered segments. For example, the discussion of biogeochemical cycles necessitates that biological and geological concepts be interrelated. However, in general, the lesson is structured in a linear way, each concept being discussed in detail before the next one is presented. In relation to the eight cell model, this lesson consists predominantly of a discussion of general processes as constant phenomena. This indicates classification in cell 2. There is a brief discussion of specific organisms and their selective habitation of various kinds of water masses in the section on geological influences on water quality. This brief segment should be classified in cell 7 since the discussion includes references to specific organisms, and their variable occurrence in various kinds of water. This is fundamentally a discussion of classification of environmental niches and their specific inhabitants. Conceptually this falls in the category of structures as explained in Chapter One and hence the reason for classifying it in cell 7.

In general, one would expect a lesson on interactions among living things to be largely a discussion of processes (mechanisms of interaction) and that some cluster-centered segments would be used to illustrate the interrelationships of the various components of the system.

The preceding sample lessons have illustrated various ways of organizing content for reception learning. With the exception of the lesson on cell membrane models, the purpose of the lessons was to convey knowledge of facts and principles and to illustrate application of principles to various specific biological problems. The lesson on cell membrane models was particularly designed to illustrate the use of various cognitive skills in scientific inquiry.

The Biological Sciences Curriculum Study Committee has prepared some clever lessons to stimulate classroom discussion on various topics of scientific enquiry. These are published as "Invitations to Enquiry" in the *Biology Teachers Handbook* edited by J. J. Schwab. Many of the American Institute of Biological Sciences publications also contain laboratory exercises and extended laboratory experiences called laboratory blocks which encourage student problem solving and creative investigations. Genetics lessons provide a unique opportunity for teachers to create problem-solving discussion tasks; an example of such a discussion task is given in Appendix D.

Chapter Four

ANALYZING THE ORGANIZATION OF CLASSROOM DISCOURSE

A well planned lesson with clearly defined objectives has a greater probability of succeeding than one that is less well prepared. But even with the most carefully planned preparatory work, some lessons fail to achieve the objectives intended by the teacher or students. It is wise to occasionally perform a critical analysis to determine how effectively a lesson has been presented—to determine, among other things, how well the objectives of the lesson have been met. Such self analysis can help a teacher recognize points of difficulty in achieving lesson objectives. Analysis of a lesson based on one's memory of what has occurred is seldom complete or accurate. Even with the greatest effort to be objective and honest in recall, our expectations and biases influence our judgment and produce an erroneous conclusion about the organization of the lesson. Advisers to teachers benefit by sometimes applying a more objective method of analysis than can be rendered by mere overall judgmental analysis. The purpose of this chapter is to describe various ways of obtaining an objective analysis of classroom discourse.

We should recognize at the outset that many of these techniques are designed to assess specific qualities of classroom discourse and their exclusive application is not recommended. That is to say, the methods described here will help you gain some insight into specific properties of classroom verbal behavior, but these should not be considered the only qualities of significance.

All of the analytical categories are derived from the objectives and principles of lesson organization presented in this book. There are other parameters to which the teacher should be sensitive, such as the inherent interest value of the material to the students, and the likelihood that the organization of ideas arouses student interest in ways other than those described in this book. For example, the content presented can be important in maintaining pupil interest. The question should be asked, is it related in some measure to the pupils own domain of experience—that is, relevant to problems of maturation, biological processes, community affairs, or intrinsic interests verbalized by the pupils? Any classroom experience which seems to arouse unusually excellent pupil dialogue, creativity, or problem-solving skills should be analyzed to determine possible causes for these outcomes. These causal factors may involve socio-emotional variables or classroom group organizational parameters. The teacher should be sensitive to the emotional and socio-psychological factors in classroom organization in addition to the content-based parameters presented in this book. Above all else, the teacher should be flexible in designing various learning experiences and in applying techniques of self-analysis. In this chapter, various empirical methods of analyzing the organization of verbal classroom content are discussed and illustrated. The techniques of analyzing classroom discourse are presented as follows: 1) methods of recording classroom discourse; 2) identifying the kind of cognitive operations used in classroom discourse based on the *Taxonomy of Educational Objectives* (Bloom et al.); 3) analyzing content structure; and 4) application of the eight cell model in analyzing content organization.

A record of classroom discourse can be obtained by placing a casette tape recorder in a central position in the classroom, the microphone on a thick felt pad or sponge rubber support to minimize picking up extraneous sounds. It is usually necessary to set the amplitude knob to maximum in order to pick up student comments. This is particularly true if the microphone is near the front of the room. It is also wise to point the microphone toward the class. This facilitates reception of both teacher and pupil discourse. You need to experiment with various locations for the microphone in your classroom to get the best recording. Rooms vary in acoustical properties which makes it almost impossible to predict where a microphone should be placed to achieve the best results. If the class is operating in small groups, then you will find it necessary to place the microphone near the particular group to be analyzed, or provide several tape recorders to obtain a record of the discussion in each group. If you are a visitor in a classroom (observer or teacher adviser), some of the data collection can be performed during the period of observation. For a more thorough examination of a lesson, it is wise to obtain a tape recording.

There are two methodological concepts of which you should be aware when performing classroom analyses. They are the concepts of *validity* and *reliability*. An observation is considered valid to the extent that it accurately represents a particular phenomenon being observed. For example, if one has a check list to be used in recording pupil problem-solving behavior with particular reference to the use of hypotheses and experimental design techniques, one would like the instrument to accurately reflect such activity. If the check list categories are improperly defined or too narrowly defined to allow accurate classification of an instance of hypothesis-making or an activity properly called experimental design, then the instrument is not valid for the purposes it was intended. Validity, therefore, is the extent to which an observation instrument allows accurate categorization of the phenomena it is supposed to assess. In some cases, the observation instrument is insufficiently sensitive to allow a full classification of the events it is supposed to assess. There may not be enough categories in the instrument or they may be improperly labeled thereby reducing the observer's sensitivity to the kinds of behaviors that should be classified by the use of the instrument. Sometimes a potentially valid observation instrument is violated simply because the behaviors to be included in each category are not sufficiently explained in the instructions, or insufficient operational examples are provided to allow precise categorization of observed instances. When applying a check list or other kinds of observation schedules, it is wise to carefully examine the definitions and descriptions of the categories and the behaviors they represent before beginning an actual analysis. Observation instrument validity can be determined by examining its face validity; that is, inspecting the categories and their definitions to determine if they accurately represent the kind and range of phenomena to be classified. Alternatively, concurrent validity can be obtained if a comparable instrument of a different form exists that is known to be valid. Both instruments are used to assess classroom behavior and the results obtained from each one are compared. The trial instrument is considered valid to the extent that its results correlate with the standard instrument.

The interobserver reliability in using an observation instrument can be obtained as follows. Two or more trained observers use the instrument to assess the same lesson. The results of their analyses are compared. The interobserver reliability is the amount of agreement among the observers in their categorization of the phenomenon. A coefficient of agreement can be reported. It is the ratio of the number of categories on which the observers agree to the total number of categories marked. Thus, if the total number of categories marked in a check list is 10, and only 8 of these are marked by all observers, then the coefficient of agreement is $8/10 = 0.80$. There is 80 per cent agreement. A minimal level of 80 per cent agreement is usually desired. For purposes of analyzing your own lessons, it is not necessary to obtain validity and reliability data. If, however, you plan to perform a serious research study using classroom observation instruments, it is wise to obtain reliability and validity data.

IDENTIFYING COGNITIVE PROCESSES IN CLASSROOM DISCOURSE

A convenient check list (Chart 5) can be assembled to assess the cognitive processes used in classroom discourse based on the categories in the cognitive domain of the *Taxonomy of Educational Objectives.* When a lesson is organized with an objective of using one or more cognitive categories cited in the list of outcome objectives (Chapter One), it is helpful to know to what extent classroom discourse actually reflects the use of those categories. If a lesson is intended to communicate knowledge of concepts and principles, one would like to know to what extent these cognitive knowledge categories are used. On the other hand, if certain cognitive skills are to be presented, we would like to know what part of the lesson is devoted to these cognitive processes. The check list in Chart 5 can be used for this purpose. In this chart, the horizontal rows represent categories in the taxonomy. Knowledge categories are listed at the top half of the left-hand column and cognitive skills appear in the bottom of the list. The colums represent minute-long intervals of time. During each minute of classroom discourse, a mark is placed in the appropriate space when an utterance is heard belonging to that category. It is best to mark the space immediately upon hearing the utterance rather than waiting until the end of the minute interval. If there is reason to keep a separate record of teacher utterances as opposed to those of pupils, then a P is placed in the space when a pupil speaks and a T when the teacher speaks. For example, if during the first minute of discourse a pupil utters a statement containing an application of a principle to a specific problem, then a P should be placed in the square opposite application in column 1. As soon as a minute interval has been completed, then the next column is begun and marked when an appropriate utterance is heard. If during a particular interval, no relevant cognitive utterances are made that can be classified in one of the row boxes, then, of course, the column remains empty. For example, the teacher may spend a minute arranging demonstration materials or reading from a great scientist's biography a statement which conveys little cognitive content, but is intended to stimulate pupil interest in the work of the scientist. When the marking of the sheet is completed, the pattern of marks established among the rows indicates to what extent particular categories were used. One may also compute a crude estimate of the percentage of time devoted to any particular cognitive category by dividing the *total* number of columns used into the number of marked spaces in the chart. Suppose, for example, that a lesson lasts 30 minutes. Therefore, 30 columns are used. Assume that the teacher utters statements containing concepts in 10 of the minute intervals. The percentage of minute intervals devoted to this kind

Chart 5

A Check List of Cognitive Categories

categories	*minutes*																			
Knowledge	**1**	**2**	**3**	**4**	**5**	**6**	**7**	**8**	**9**	**10**	**11**	**12**	**13**	**14**	**15**	**16**	**17**	**18**	**19**	**20**
of Specifics																				
of Processes																				
of Principles																				
of Concepts																				
of Theories																				
Skills																				
Translation																				
Interpretation																				
Extrapolation																				
Application																				
Analysis of Elements																				
Analysis of Relationships																				
Analysis of Organizational Principles																				
Synthesis																				
Evaluation																				

of content is 33 per cent ($10/30 \times 100$). Similar coefficients can be obtained for all other categories in Chart 6. The chart is useful for general analyses of lessons when one wants to gain an idea of how well various cognitive categories are utilized in a lesson. Pupil and teacher usage of categories can be computed separately for percentages for each, or the two can be combined to yield a composite percentage.

An analysis of a junior high school biology class is shown in Chart 6. Twenty minutes of classroom discourse are analyzed. The instances of teacher use of categories are marked with a T and pupil use marked with a P. The percentage duration of each cognitive category was compiled at the end of the analysis. The percentages for teacher and pupil utterances are reported in the far right-hand column. These figures represent the per cent of minute intervals containing an utterance falling within a category. For teacher utterances, 85 per cent of the minute intervals contained references to specific facts, 40 per cent contained concept statements, 20 per cent principles, and 5 per cent contained process statements. Pupil utterances of specific facts occurred in 35 per cent of the minute intervals, and utterances of processes and concepts each occurred in 5 per cent of the minute intervals. The chart shows that the teacher talked most of the time and that within the knowledge categories, specific facts, concepts, and principles were the major categories represented. Within the skill categories, the teacher utterances were classified as follows: analysis of relationships—20 per cent; analysis of elements—10 per cent; and analysis of organizational principles—5 per cent. Pupil utterances occurred once in the evaluation category (5 per cent of the minute intervals). It is clear that most of the minute intervals contain references to knowledge categories. The presentation of skill categories by the teacher occurred largely in the first half of the lesson. Thereafter, most of the utterances were categorized as knowledge statements. It is interesting to note that a student introduced a process statement at the eighteenth minute interval, but the teacher did not follow through on that idea.

It is not uncommon to find lessons heavily weighted toward the knowledge categories. The reader is cautioned to be alert to this possibility in analyzing his own lessons. Obviously, if an

Chart 6

A Check List of Cognitive Categories: SAMPLE ANALYSIS

categories	*minutes* 1	2	3	4	5	6	7	8	9	10	11	12	13	14	15	16	17	18	19	20	*percentage duration* T	P
Knowledge																						
of Specifics	T	T				T	T	T	T/P	T	T	T	T	T/P	T/P	T/P	T/P	T/P	T/P	T	85	35
of Processes		T																P			5	5
of Principles							T	T	T			T									20	
of Concepts	T/P			T	T									T	T	T		T	T		40	5
of Theories																						
Skills																						
Translation																						
Interpretation																						
Extrapolation																						
Application																						
Analysis of Elements		T	T																		10	
Analysis of Relationships		T							T	T		T									20	
Analysis of Organizational Principles												T									5	
Synthesis																						
Evaluation			P																			5

inordinate amount of time is spent on teaching knowledge to the exclusion of cognitive skills, some additional attention should be given to skill acquisition. It is also obvious that the lesson analyzed in Chart 6 contains predominately teacher utterances. If, during analysis of one's lessons, a large number of lessons appear to be teacher dominated, the question should be asked whether this is desirable. Clearly, students can learn communication skills and actively participate in group problem solving only when they are given the opportunity to participate in dialogue. The check list is useful in assessing the amount of substantive contribution students make to a class.

You should be aware of certain weaknesses in the instrument. Information about the duration of discourse falling in a particular category is not exact. Since categories are marked during one minute intervals, we do not know whether the content lasted only a few seconds during that minute interval or extended for the full minute. Our resolution of duration of the marked events is limited to one minute. Therefore, we cannot compute precise time durations of utterances falling within a cognitive category. Moreover, the instrument is accurate only to the extent that the observer properly identifies and categorizes an event. The cognitive categories of the *Taxonomy of Educational Objectives* are not always easily and precisely identified when listening to classroom discourse. There may be some ambiguity for example as to whether the discourse contains conceptual statements or statements of principles. To help you achieve greater precision in identifying knowledge categories, some simple definitions of specific facts, processes, principles, concepts, and theories are given. A specific fact is a statement containing a definition of terms, citation of a particular structure or a reference to a specific event in time. These are statements which deal with concrete instances or specific categories of immediate experience. Processes are sequences of events occurring in time. They include the interaction among and sequential ordering of specific events. Any statement of a trend or sequence falls in this category. A principle is a general rule or invariant relationship. The various laws of science fall within this category. A concept is a generalization—a definition of a category of objects or events at a higher level of abstraction than a specific fact. Concepts include categories such as ecosystem, adaptation, gene, phenotype, genotype, skeleton, and enzyme activity. If, of course, one refers to a specific ecosystem, or a particular animal skeleton, for example, the proper category is specifics. A theory is a generalized and sometimes abstract explanation of a set of relationships. This includes concepts and principles interrelated in such a way as to explain natural phenomena. A model of cell membrane structure, the theory of evolution, or the theory of kinetic-molecular motion are examples falling within the category of theories.

Identification of cognitive skills in classroom discourse can be quite difficult unless some clearly established rules are followed. For science lessons, I have found the following useful in making classification decisions for the cognitive skill categories. As a general guideline: a cognitive skill is marked in the check list only when an overt expression of it is observed. Each cognitive skill category will be considered in greater detail.

Translation occurs when some verbal, pictorial, or quantitative communication is presented in a second set of terms. In other words, the speaker must actually set forth the material to be translated and then demonstrate the translation by rendering a part-for-part restatement of the communication in different terminology. This may be, for example, presenting a chart and verbally identifying the components, or translating chemical or mathematical formulas into verbal terms. I do not mark the category space unless the teacher or pupil actually demonstrates the skill in their verbal utterance. *Interpretation* is an act of identifying and explaining a verbal, pictorial, or mathematical presentation. An explanation of the meaning of a chart, or a passage in a scientific report, or a mathematical expression constitutes interpretation. Again, the speaker must actually carry out the act of interpretation for it to be classified in that category on the check list. *Extrapolation* is an utterance demonstrating the extension of trends and sequences beyond the data available or making predictions about later events from preceding events. This may occur as an extension of graphic data, making predictions from theory, or extending trends such as growth rates, lines of evolutionary development, and so forth. *Application* occurs when the speaker clearly uses a rule or principle to solve a problem or to produce a conclusion. This is most clearly identified when the speaker states a rule or principle and then demonstrates its use in reaching a conclusion. The use in a genetics lesson of a Punnett square (checkerboard) technique for predicting the genotypes of offspring is an example of application. *Analysis* is the identification of component parts (elements), or interactions and associations among component parts (relationships), and the identification of organizational plans and arrangements of parts (organizational principles). If the teacher presents a complex chart and identifies the components as entities, he has analyzed the elements. If the components are identified and interrelated—the mutual influences and/or spatial relationships among them given—analysis of relationships has been carried out. A discussion of the rationale, or generalized plan for a presentation as seen in a chart or a model, or a method of analysis in science are instances of analyses of organizational principles. *Synthesis* occurs when the speaker is clearly bringing together several diverse content areas and creating a model or plan. This may be the creation of a descriptive model of a scientific phenomenon, or a plan of work as a proposed way of performing an experiment. *Evaluation* is a statement of judgment about the value of a presentation relative to some criterion. For example, stating the possible value of an experiment plan in terms of the likelihood that the experiment will yield meaningful results is evaluation.

It is wise to prepare sample lists of ideas falling within each of the categories before beginning an analysis of a lesson. This is particularly useful when a teacher is analyzing his own lessons. He knows, hopefully, with a fair degree of precision what specific facts, processes, principles, concepts, and theories were to be included in the lesson. Making up a preliminary list of ideas falling within each category helps the coding of the lesson to proceed more efficiently. One has only to listen for these categories, and any others related to them, and mark the appropriate box in the check list. A similar list of cognitive skill instances can be prepared. When marking skill categories on the check list, one must be aware that statements containing evidence of cognitive skills may be very complex and involve several kinds of skill. If more than one kind of skill is clearly contained in the verbalization, then both should be marked on the check list. For example, if the speaker states an extrapolation while preparing a synthesis of several ideas, both categories should be marked. If there is no statement of a lower order category while developing a higher order skill, then only the higher order skill is marked. This is true even if you can infer the need for a lower order cognitive skill to reach the ultimate verbalized skill. *Only actual verbalizations are coded.* When an utterance falling in a cognitive category is begun during a one-minute interval and extends over into the next minute interval, both interval boxes are marked opposite the appropriate category. You will find it helpful to practice with some preliminary lessons before starting a serious analysis.

The Content Structure of Classroom Discourse

The structure of classroom discourse can be analyzed using B_1 and B_2 coefficients as explained in Chapters Two and Three. Each statement of discourse must be analyzed. Only teacher statements are analyzed here, although both teacher and student statements can be analyzed by this technique. To facilitate discourse analysis, a check list is prepared as shown in Chart 7.

Columns represent discourse statement. It is important to note that we use statements of discourse as the unit of analysis and not minute intervals as was used in the Cognitive Categories Check List (Charts 5 and 6). As each statement is heard, the substantive terms appearing for the first time are entered in the list on the left-hand side of the chart and a check mark is placed in the box opposite the word, and, of course, within the proper column representing the statement number. Thereafter, when the same word appears in subsequent statements, a check mark is placed in the box opposite the word. In this manner, the list of terms to be coded is compiled as the lesson unfolds, and the coding proceeds simultaneously. The check list in Chart 7 is complete for 29 statements of the sample lesson. The B_1 coefficients are listed at the bottom of each column. An examination of the check list will show how it has been compiled. The

Chart 7
Content Structure Check List

technical words / *statement number*	1	2	3	4	5	6	7	8	9	10	11	12	13	14	15	16	17	18	19	20	21	22	23	24	25	26	27	28	29
1 Animals	X		X	X		X	X													X									
2 Specimens	X															X		X	X		X	X	X	X		X	X		
3 Diversity		X																											
4 Variation			X																										
5 Plants					X																								
6 Biology Textbook						X	X																						
7 System of Organization							X																			X			
8 Characteristics							X			X			X																
9 Mammal								X	X																				
10 Mouse								X	X	X																			
11 Bat								X	X	X																			
12 Pig								X	X	X																			
13 Insects											X	X	X	X															
14 Butterfly											X																		
15 Moth											X																		
16 Grouped												X		X															
17 Jars (specimen)															X														
18 Formaldehyde																X													
19 Alcohol																X													
20 Preserved																X	X	X											
21 Water																		X											
22 Time																			X										
23 Rot (decay)																			X										
24 Kill																				X					X				
25 Die																				X									
26 Dissect																						X	X						
27 Scientific Name																											X		
28 Common Name																											X	X	
29 Name (general)																												X	
30 Know																													X
B_i Coefficients		0.0	0.0	0.67	0.0	0.0	0.67	0.0	1.0	0.75	0.0	0.40	0.50	0.50	0.0	0.0	0.40	0.50	0.33	0.0	0.0	0.67	1.00	0.67	0.0	0.0	0.40	0.40	0.0

first statement contained a reference to animals and specimens. Therefore these two spaces were marked in column 1. Statement 2 contains a reference to diversity and therefore a mark is placed in box 3 of column 2. Statement 3 contains a reference to animals and their variation—marks are placed in boxes 1 and 4 of column 3. This procedure is continued until all of the statements have been analyzed. Each consecutive pair of statements is then analyzed to compute B_1 coefficients. In the first two pairs, there are no matched words (there is no commonality in the statement pairs), therefore $B_1=0.0$. However, statement 4 contains one word in common with statement 3, the word *animals*. An unmatched word (*variation*) appears in statement 3. The B_1 coefficient formula as presented in Chapter Two is:

$$B_1=\frac{n_1}{n_0+n_1}$$

The term n_1 is the number of times a matched word occurs in a pair of statements. Statements 3 and 4 each contain the word *animals*. The word *animals* occurs two times, so $n_1=2$ for this pair of statements. The term n_0 is the number of unmatched elements in a pair of statements. Here, n_0 is 1 because there is only one unmatched word (*variation*). Therefore, $B_1=2/1+2$. The B_1 value is $2/3=0.67$. This process is continued until the whole lesson or specified part thereof is analyzed. The mean B_1 for the lesson can be obtained by adding all of the B_1 values and dividing this total by their number.

The Content Structure Check List also is useful in determining the sequential pattern of a lesson. Serial-centered lessons produce a distribution of marks as shown in Chart 7. The marks tend to fall along a narrow diagonal across the chart. There are few marks scattered in the upper right or lower left parts of the chart. The lesson analyzed in Chart 7 also has a consistent pattern of marks falling in the line labeled *Specimen*. This indicates that the lesson is organized around a theme of animal specimens beginning at statement 16. A cluster-centered lesson, in contrast, has a diffuse pattern of marks falling around the diagonal. This indicates, as would be expected in a cluster-centered lesson, that multiple relationships are being made as the lesson unfolds. It indicates further that previously used ideas are being integrated with ideas presented subsequently in the lesson. The flow of ideas in the lesson becomes apparent by following the trend of marks in the Content Structure Check List. The sample lesson analyzed in Chart 7 begins with a discussion of diversity and variation among plants and animals as general concepts. The lesson proceeds to a discussion of mammalian and insect characteristics, and continues with a discussion of the properties of preserved specimens. It is not necessary to plot Kinetograms unless a more detailed analysis of the lesson is required. A general description of the procedure will be given here. A thorough discussion of Kinetogram production and analysis is presented in *Quantitative Analysis of Structure in Teaching* (Anderson 1971), which also contains time-saving methods of analysis.

To construct a Kinetogram, you must first compute B_2 values for each consecutive pair of statements in a lesson. Toward this end, the total frequency of occurrence of all terms used in the lesson must be obtained. These are computed by adding up the marks in each row and recording the number at the end of that row. For example, in Chart 7, the word *animals* is used 6 times, and *specimens* is used 10 times. Frequencies are compiled for all rows. Then, a B_2 value is computed for each pair of statements where a B_1 was computed. The formula for B_2 given in Chapter Two is:

$$B_2 = 1 - \left[\frac{n_0}{n_0 + n_1} \cdot \left(\frac{F' + F''}{\Sigma f} \right)^{\frac{1}{2}} \right]$$

In this formula, the term n_0/n_0+n_1 is equivalent to $1-B_1$, and can be obtained by using the B_1 values computed for each pair of statements. To obtain the potency term $(F'+F''/\Sigma f)^{\frac{1}{2}}$, you identify the unmatched words in the first column of a pair and obtain the total frequency of each in the lesson. You then select that total frequency which is greatest and substitute that number for F'. In like manner you examine the second column of the pair and find the total frequency of highest value for an unmatched word in that column. The frequency value is substituted for F''. The total frequency of all elements (sum of the row totals) is substituted each time for Σf. Then, the solution is computed. The B_2

coefficient is found in this manner for each pair of statements in the lesson. When all B_2 values have been completed, they are plotted as illustrated in Figures 18 and 19 of Chapter Three. The abscissa at the top of the graph is divided into units representing statements uttered by the teacher and/or students depending on whose discourse is being analyzed. The ordinate is divided into B_2 units. The B_2 values are plotted on the graph and connected by lines. Analyses of lesson structure can be performed as explained in Chapter Two and illustrated in Chapter Three.

If you do not plot a Kinetogram, the Content Structure Check List contains sufficient information to obtain (1) the overall mean B_1 for a lesson, (2) the organizational plan of a lesson, whether it is serial-centered or cluster-centered, and (3) the identification of discourse spans. These are blocks of discourse (as explained in Chapters Two and Three) where one or more persistent ideas provide continuity within a sequence of statements. For example, in Chart 7, there is a preliminary introduction of rather diffuse content in statements 1 to 16. Thereafter, a clearly recognizable span of content begins and runs to statement 28. The continuity of this span is produced by a discussion of *specimens* as shown by the clearly discernible set of marks falling within row 2 on the chart. Once a span has been identified, the mean B_1 can be computed. The major ideas in the span should also be cited to allow analysis of content flow.

When planning a lesson, one should give careful attention to the structure to be used in various parts. In some places, high structure (high commonality, continuity of ideas) may be desirable to effectively enhance acquisition of the content. At other points in the lesson, the structure can be reduced to allow multiple relationships or highly diverse content to arouse pupil interest and stimulate discussion. The content structural analyses described here allows you to estimate how well you have achieved these organizational objectives.

Application of the Eight Cell Model to Analysis of Classroom Discourse

The categories (cells) in the eight cell model discussed in Chapter One can be used to determine the kind and sequence of content in a lesson. Toward this end a Content Category Check List has been prepared as shown in Chart 8. The left-hand column contains a list of the characteristics for each cell in the eight cell model. The vertical columns represent minute intervals as they did on the Cognitive Categories Check List. The check list in Chart 8 is used as follows. For each minute of classroom discourse, the observer determines which of the eight categories in the left-hand list best represents organization of the discourse. A mark is placed in the space opposite the category and in the column appropriate for that time interval. One must listen carefully to the discourse in order to properly classify it according to the properties contained in the list. It is wise to listen for nearly a full minute and then mark the appropriate space. The most efficient and logical way of making a decision is to determine first whether the content is largely made up of specifics or of generalities. If specifics, then the content is classified in the lower half of the check list (cells 5 through 8). On the other hand, if the content is made up of generalities, it falls within the upper half of the list (cells 1 through 4). The next question to ask is whether the content is presented as constants (invariants) or as variables (undergoing variation during time or among various categories being discussed). The answer further limits the final choice to two categories—structures or processes. When this decision is reached, the content is fully specified in terms of the check list and a mark is placed in the appropriate box. There are some precautions which should be kept in mind while analyzing a lesson with this instrument. First, the definitions of the categories must be clearly understood. *Structures* include categories of objects or physical entities such as components of a system. *Processes* are time correlated events (trends and sequences). *Specifics* are citations to particular categories: specific objects, concrete examples, or single isolated events. *Generalities* are inclusive or highly general representations of structures or processes. General categories, or general models of a process or phenomenon occurring in "all living things" are classified as generalities. *Constants* are features or events that are presented as invariant, not being altered or abolished by other events. *Variables* are ideas presented as discontinuous phenomena—things that occur at some times, but not at others. It is not necessary that the speaker in the lesson identify the influencing factor that causes the variation. Obviously, however, a good lesson should include a discussion of the sources and causes of variation as well as the variable phenomenon itself. Second, the analyst must attend to the overall organization of the discourse during the minute interval and make a general estimate of the classification of the content. Finally, I find it helpful to use the last ten seconds of the minute interval to make a decision about the classification of the content and to mark the check list before the next minute interval begins. This increases the likelihood that most of the discourse in the new minute interval will be heard without interference from activities spilling over from the previous interval.

An examination of Chart 8 shows that most of the teacher's discourse is classified in cell 1 and cell 5. This is a discussion of structures at a general level and then at a specific level. At one point, in the sixth and seventh minute intervals, the discussion turned toward variations in animal structures at the specific level and for only one minute interval (at the second minute) the discourse contained a discussion of processes. This is in agreement with the classification of the same interval in Chart 6 where the second minute interval is coded in a process cognitive category. The two analyses, of course, were performed at different times. Chart 8, however, tells us more than Chart 6, namely, that the process was discussed at a general level and that variations in its occurrence were described. The discussion concerned various ways in which animals were preserved for laboratory examination. The various kinds of preserving processes were described and the variable effects on tissue preservation were discussed. In all, the lesson consists largely of description of animal structures and the categories to which various specific animals are assigned. The Content Category Check List can be used to determine the

Chart 8

Content Category Check List

categories	*minutes*																						
	1	2	3	4	5	6	7	8	9	10	11	12	13	14	15	16	17	18	19	20	21		
Cell 1: Constants, Structures, Generalities	X		X	X	X			X	X			X	X						X	X			
Cell 2: Constants, Processes, Generalities																							
Cell 3: Variables, Structures, Generalities																							
Cell 4: Variables, Processes, Generalities		X																					
Cell 5: Constants, Structures, Specifics										X	X			X	X	X	X	X					
Cell 6: Constants, Processes, Specifics																							
Cell 7: Variables, Structures, Specifics						X	X																
Cell 8: Variables Processes, Specifics																							

diversity and flexibility of lesson organization. If most lessons are consistently organized around the same categories, the teacher may want to consider whether some careful thought should be given to developing alternative lesson plans.

In conclusion, the thrust of this chapter is to recommend that the teacher occasionally tape record a lesson and analyze it as described here. Some of the techniques presented are admittedly not rigorous, but are sufficiently accurate to yield objective feedback as to how effectively lesson organizational objectives are achieved. The results of these analyses, within the context of the general advice given in the introduction to this chapter, should yield insights about organizing lessons more flexibly and creatively. Prospective teachers and education students may find the techniques presented here useful tools when observing classrooms. The instruments may also be used by education students when analyzing audio or video tape recordings of classroom verbal behavior. The ideas of modern biology provide a rich opportunity to explore new ways of organizing content for classroom presentation. I hope some of the practical ideas shared with you in this book will enrich your experiences as a teacher and bring greater appreciation for the value of self analysis toward the improvement of science teaching.

APPENDICES

Appendix A Words Coded in Lessons One and Two

1 living cell
2 assemblage
3 molecules
4 function
5 nucleic acids
6 storing
7 transmitting
8 information
9 linked or bonded
10 code or code sequence
11 morse code
12 telegraphy
13 organization
14 production or synthesis
15 organelles
16 structural molecules
17 structure
18 nitrogenous bases
19 ring compound
20 carbon or carbon atom
21 hydrogen
22 nitrogen
23 oxygen
24 pyrimidine
25 purines
26 atom or atomic
27 name
28 cytosine
29 uracil
30 thymine
31 adenine
32 guanine
33 sugar molecule
34 ribose
35 deoxyribose
36 hydroxyl
37 covalent bond
38 nucleoside
39 adenosine
40 guanosine
41 cytidine
42 uridine
43 thymidine
44 nucleotide
45 phosphate
46 ester linkage
47 alcohol group
48 acid
49 phosphoric acid
50 phosphoester
51 characteristic
52 biological specificity
53 code function
54 dinucleotide
55 phosphodiester linkage
56 *di-*
57 polynucleotide
58 hundreds
59 poly
60 pattern
61 DNA strand
62 RNA strand
63 nucleus
64 cytoplasm
65 double helix
66 cross-linkage
67 strand
68 base-pair linkage
69 bridge
70 hydrogen bond
71 spatial relation
72 protein
73 amino acid
74 protein synthesizing site or ribosome
75 process
76 translate
77 messenger RNA
78 transfer RNA
79 template
80 surface
81 globular protein
82 anticodon
83 binding site
84 folding
85 structural unit
86 enzyme or catalyst
87 chemical process
88 life or living system
89 communicate
90 animals
91 song
92 birds
93 sounds
94 insects
95 language
96 man
97 smell
98 sense
99 time
100 stable
101 evidence
102 responds
103 organism
104 hormones
105 body functions

106	balance	112	cell growth	118	combinations
107	activity	113	differentiation	119	chloroplasts
108	organs	114	metabolism	120	mitochondrion
109	message	115	cellular distribution	121	source
110	body	116	similarities	122	transfer
111	regulating or control	117	differ	123	codon

Appendix B Code Summary Sheet for Lesson One

1)	1	2	3	4	0	0	0	0	0	
2)	3	5	4	6	7	8	1	0	0	
3)	5	8	3	9	0	0	0	0	0	
4)	5	10	11	12	0	0	0	0	0	
5)	11	8	0	0	0	0	0	0	0	1 nucleic acids
6)	1	3	5	8	13	4	14	16	15	
7)	17	5	0	0	0	0	0	0	0	
8)	17	5	3	0	0	0	0	0	0	
9)	5	3	18	0	0	0	0	0	0	
10)	18	19	20	21	22	23	0	0	0	
11)	18	24	25	0	0	0	0	0	0	
12)	24	22	19	0	0	0	0	0	0	
13)	25	0	0	0	0	0	0	0	0	
14)	25	19	0	0	0	0	0	0	0	
15)	19	24	26	3	20	22	0	0	0	2 nitrogenous bases
16)	26	24	27	0	0	0	0	0	0	
17)	24	28	29	30	0	0	0	0	0	
18)	24	22	23	20	19	0	0	0	0	
19)	25	22	23	0	0	0	0	0	0	
20)	22	25	31	0	0	0	0	0	0	
21)	32	22	23	25	0	0	0	0	0	

22)	5	18	33	34	0	0	0	0	0	
23)	24	25	34	0	0	0	0	0	0	
24)	20	34	0	0	0	0	0	0	0	
25)	34	35	3	0	0	0	0	0	0	
26)	34	35	26	20	0	0	0	0	0	3 ribose
27)	34	36	20	0	0	0	0	0	0	
28)	35	34	23	0	0	0	0	0	0	
29)	34	24	25	20	0	0	0	0	0	
30)	24	25	37	20	0	0	0	0	0	
31)	3	25	24	34	38	0	0	0	0	
32)	27	38	18	9	34	0	0	0	0	
33)	25	39	40	31	32	38	0	0	0	
34)	24	38	41	42	43	28	29	30	0	4 nucleoside
35)	33	34	35	18	0	0	0	0	0	
36)	31	32	9	34	35	0	0	0	0	
37)	28	34	35	9	0	0	0	0	0	
38)	29	9	34	30	35	0	0	0	0	
39)	38	44	0	0	0	0	0	0	0	
40)	44	38	45	20	34	0	0	0	0	
41)	45	20	46	0	0	0	0	0	0	
42)	46	9	47	48	0	0	0	0	0	
43)	44	49	46	47	20	38	34	0	0	
44)	46	45	50	0	0	0	0	0	0	
45)	51	38	45	50	0	0	0	0	0	
46)	18	44	52	0	0	0	0	0	0	
47)	52	53	3	0	0	0	0	0	0	
48)	44	10	0	0	0	0	0	0	0	
49)	18	52	44	0	0	0	0	0	0	
50)	44	24	25	0	0	0	0	0	0	5 nucleotide
51)	44	9	0	0	0	0	0	0	0	
52)	44	10	0	0	0	0	0	0	0	
53)	44	10	3	0	0	0	0	0	0	
54)	44	45	20	0	0	0	0	0	0	
55)	44	36	20	0	0	0	0	0	0	
56)	44	9	54	0	0	0	0	0	0	
57)	45	44	46	36	20	0	0	0	0	
58)	46	55	45	44	0	0	0	0	0	
59)	56	0	0	0	0	0	0	0	0	
60)	9	46	45	0	0	0	0	0	0	
61)	9	55	0	0	0	0	0	0	0	
62)	3	9	54	0	0	0	0	0	0	

63)	57	0	0	0	0	0	0	0	0	
64)	57	3	44	0	0	0	0	0	0	
65)	57	3	44	58	0	0	0	0	0	
66)	57	27	44	0	0	0	0	0	0	
67)	59	0	0	0	0	0	0	0	0	6 poly-
68)	57	44	0	0	0	0	0	0	0	nucleotide
69)	57	24	25	44	0	0	0	0	0	
70)	57	44	60	9	0	0	0	0	0	
71)	57	3	0	0	0	0	0	0	0	
72)	57	3	35	44	61	0	0	0	0	
73)	61	0	0	0	0	0	0	0	0	
74)	61	0	0	0	0	0	0	0	0	
75)	57	62	0	0	0	0	0	0	0	
76)	62	0	0	0	0	0	0	0	0	7 DNA strand
77)	62	44	34	0	0	0	0	0	0	and
78)	61	62	18	33	0	0	0	0	0	RNA strand
79)	62	29	61	30	0	0	0	0	0	
80)	61	62	0	0	0	0	0	0	0	
81)	62	34	29	0	0	0	0	0	0	
82)	61	35	30	0	0	0	0	0	0	
83)	61	63	62	64	1	0	0	0	0	
84)	61	65	66	18	67	0	0	0	0	
85)	67	38	9	45	57	0	0	0	0	
86)	44	57	18	0	0	0	0	0	0	
87)	45	33	57	18	66	0	0	0	0	
88)	57	65	68	0	0	0	0	0	0	
89)	31	9	30	32	28	0	0	0	0	
90)	66	18	0	0	0	0	0	0	0	
91)	18	60	21	23	0	0	0	0	0	
92)	21	23	3	69	0	0	0	0	0	8 poly-
93)	69	70	0	0	0	0	0	0	0	nucleotide
94)	70	21	23	71	0	0	0	0	0	
95)	31	30	28	32	21	23	57	0	0	
96)	31	32	30	29	70	0	0	0	0	
97)	65	61	70	66	67	0	0	0	0	
98)	62	61	3	0	0	0	0	0	0	
99)	62	65	0	0	0	0	0	0	0	
100)	61	62	24	25	34	38	44	0	0	
101)	26	3	71	57	61	62	0	0	0	
102)	57	6	7	8	0	0	0	0	0	

103)	44	61	72	1	0	0	0	0	0	
104)	61	44	0	0	0	0	0	0	0	
105)	44	72	73	0	0	0	0	0	0	
106)	61	60	0	0	0	0	0	0	0	
107)	18	72	0	0	0	0	0	0	0	
108)	8	61	10	72	76	0	0	0	0	
109)	75	76	61	62	74	64	0	0	0	
110)	62	72	14	0	0	0	0	0	0	
111)	62	77	78	0	0	0	0	0	0	9 protein
112)	77	62	0	0	0	0	0	0	0	
113)	77	61	63	0	0	0	0	0	0	
114)	77	63	64	72	14	0	0	0	0	
115)	78	62	64	0	0	0	0	0	0	
116)	78	72	73	14	0	0	0	0	0	
117)	78	73	0	0	0	0	0	0	0	
118)	78	73	14	0	0	0	0	0	0	
119)	72	14	75	0	0	0	0	0	0	

120)	61	63	77	0	0	0	0	0	0	
121)	77	44	61	0	0	0	0	0	0	
122)	61	79	77	80	0	0	0	0	0	
123)	77	62	44	61	0	0	0	0	0	
124)	7	8	61	77	0	0	0	0	0	
125)	77	63	64	0	0	0	0	0	0	
126)	64	77	74	0	0	0	0	0	0	
127)	74	64	0	0	0	0	0	0	0	
128)	74	81	77	0	0	0	0	0	0	
129)	78	73	80	77	0	0	0	0	0	
130)	78	0	0	0	0	0	0	0	0	
131)	78	73	0	0	0	0	0	0	0	
132)	78	44	10	73	0	0	0	0	0	
133)	44	10	82	0	0	0	0	0	0	
134)	82	78	77	0	0	0	0	0	0	10 messenger
135)	83	77	70	82	0	0	0	0	0	RNA
136)	78	73	77	0	0	0	0	0	0	
137)	73	71	77	18	0	0	0	0	0	
138)	73	9	77	80	0	0	0	0	0	
139)	73	78	0	0	0	0	0	0	0	
140)	73	9	72	0	0	0	0	0	0	
141)	17	72	60	84	71	0	0	0	0	
142)	17	73	72	0	0	0	0	0	0	

143)	17	72	77	0	0	0	0	0	0	10 messenger RNA (contd.)
144)	77	61	0	0	0	0	0	0	0	
145)	8	61	77	78	72	17	0	0	0	
146)	72	85	1	86	87	88	0	0	0	
147)	8	61	1	0	0	0	0	0	0	
148)	25	24	34	38	44	8	1	0	0	

Appendix C Code Summary Sheet for Lesson Two

1)	8	88	0	0	0	0	0	0	
2)	89	90	0	0	0	0	0	0	
3)	92	91	93	94	95	96	8	0	
4)	89	0	0	0	0	0	0	0	
5)	90	3	97	98	0	0	0	0	
6)	3	8	89	90	99	0	0	0	1 molecules and information
7)	8	3	100	99	0	0	0	0	
8)	3	8	7	93	0	0	0	0	
9)	101	89	90	102	3	0	0	0	
10)	103	3	104	105	106	107	108	0	
11)	104	8	3	109	110	0	0	0	
12)	1	3	6	7	8	0	0	0	
13)	3	5	0	0	0	0	0	0	
14)	5	4	111	112	113	114	0	0	
15)	5	111	114	103	105	4	1	0	2 nucleic acids
16)	5	1	0	0	0	0	0	0	
17)	17	4	5	8	3	0	0	0	
18)	5	61	62	0	0	0	0	0	
19)	61	62	17	115	4	0	0	0	
20)	61	62	116	0	0	0	0	0	3 DNA and RNA strands
21)	61	62	3	44	0	0	0	0	
22)	44	3	18	33	45	0	0	0	
23)	18	24	25	0	0	0	0	0	
24)	61	62	25	0	0	0	0	0	
25)	24	117	28	61	62	0	0	0	4 pyrimidine and purine bases
26)	24	18	20	22	21	23	19	0	
27)	22	24	0	0	0	0	0	0	
28)	26	20	19	24	0	0	0	0	

29)	25	19	24	0	0	0	0	0	
30)	19	26	24	0	0	0	0	0	
31)	24	28	29	30	0	0	0	0	4 pyrimidine and purine bases (contd.)
32)	28	22	23	9	19	0	0	0	
33)	29	23	30	20	23	0	0	0	
34)	25	31	32	0	0	0	0	0	
35)	31	22	19	32	23	0	0	0	
36)	61	62	31	32	28	0	0	0	
37)	62	29	0	0	0	0	0	0	
38)	61	30	0	0	0	0	0	0	
39)	18	117	61	62	3	33	0	0	
40)	62	34	0	0	0	0	0	0	
41)	34	23	20	19	0	0	0	0	
42)	61	33	23	0	0	0	0	0	5 ribose
43)	33	35	0	0	0	0	0	0	
44)	35	34	23	0	0	0	0	0	
45)	18	9	20	34	38	0	0	0	
46)	62	38	61	0	0	0	0	0	
47)	51	62	61	34	24	0	0	0	
48)	45	38	44	0	0	0	0	0	
49)	45	20	34	50	0	0	0	0	6 nucleoside
50)	46	14	48	47	0	0	0	0	
51)	45	48	20	47	0	0	0	0	
52)	9	50	45	0	0	0	0	0	
53)	61	62	3	57	0	0	0	0	
54)	57	44	0	0	0	0	0	0	
55)	58	44	57	0	0	0	0	0	
56)	57	59	0	0	0	0	0	0	
57)	57	44	0	0	0	0	0	0	7 polynucleotide
58)	44	54	0	0	0	0	0	0	
59)	44	9	55	20	34	0	0	0	
60)	57	45	33	18	0	0	0	0	
61)	24	25	66	57	0	0	0	0	
62)	67	9	70	0	0	0	0	0	
63)	70	9	21	23	0	0	0	0	
64)	21	23	100	9	71	0	0	0	8 hydrogen bonds
65)	61	31	30	70	32	28	0	0	

66)	18	66	21	23	100	70	0	0	8 hydrogen bonds (contd.)
67)	31	30	70	0	0	0	0	0	
68)	32	28	70	0	0	0	0	0	
69)	118	70	0	0	0	0	0	0	
70)	61	66	67	65	0	0	0	0	
71)	62	68	70	0	0	0	0	0	
72)	31	29	28	32	0	0	0	0	
73)	8	18	61	62	0	0	0	0	
74)	18	10	0	0	0	0	0	0	
75)	18	10	0	0	0	0	0	0	
76)	11	0	0	0	0	0	0	0	
77)	61	62	6	8	57	18	0	0	
78)	61	62	115	0	0	0	0	0	9 DNA and RNA strands
79)	61	63	0	0	0	0	0	0	
80)	62	64	0	0	0	0	0	0	
81)	61	119	120	1	0	0	0	0	
82)	61	57	63	0	0	0	0	0	
83)	117	4	61	62	0	0	0	0	
84)	61	121	6	8	111	1	17	4	
85)	61	111	1	4	72	14	0	0	
86)	72	1	17	3	111	114	4	0	
87)	62	77	78	0	0	0	0	0	
88)	77	61	63	64	0	0	0	0	
89)	77	10	72	14	0	0	0	0	
90)	78	3	77	0	0	0	0	0	
91)	78	4	122	72	73	85	74	0	
92)	78	73	0	0	0	0	0	0	
93)	78	73	74	0	0	0	0	0	
94)	77	3	8	0	0	0	0	0	
95)	109	77	61	74	0	0	0	0	
96)	78	3	73	77	72	14	0	0	
97)	78	9	77	123	0	0	0	0	
98)	123	18	78	82	0	0	0	0	
99)	77	78	9	80	0	0	0	0	
100)	9	80	73	72	0	0	0	0	10 messenger RNA
101)	76	61	6	8	72	14	77	0	
102)	61	111	77	17	0	0	0	0	
103)	77	17	111	9	78	80	0	0	
104)	78	73	72	17	0	0	0	0	

105)	72	4	1	0	0	0	0	0	
106)	72	85	1	13	0	0	0	0	
107)	72	86	111	114	1	0	0	0	
108)	4	5	72	1	4	0	0	0	10 messenger RNA
109)	5	8	6	122	3	0	0	0	(contd.)
110)	72	17	86	3	0	0	0	0	
111)	5	61	8	3	6	0	0	0	
112)	62	8	3	76	8	72	0	0	

Appendix D Breeder's Problems

Teaching genetics through problem-solving tasks can assume various forms from paper and pencil workbook problems to laboratory breeding tasks. Undoubtedly, the most rewarding and stimulating experiences for the student are those in the laboratory where breeding experiments are performed and analyzed. However, one limitation of laboratory work for efficient cognitive skill acquisition is the long delay between mating of the experimental organisms and the acquisition of data suitable for analysis. If laboratory projects are not available, or if additional training in problem solving is desired, breeder's problems as described here can be used. These discussion tasks allow the student to engage in intensive problem solving using simulated breeding problems. I usually use examples from plant genetics since students seem to readily accept and comprehend the phenotypic expressions. However, there is no reason why simulated laboratory problems in Drosophila genetics could not be presented in the way described here for plants. Breeder's problems is a game wherein the student assumes the role of a plant breeder who wants to produce a certain offspring. The participants in the game are told only the phenotypes of the organisms. The leader has compiled the genotypes and is in a position to inform the participants about phenotypes of the offspring produced by each simulated breeding experiment. The objective of this problem-solving task is for the participants to produce the desired combination of phenotypes in as efficient and rapid a way as possible. That is, the number of breeding steps should be kept to a minimum in producing the desired offspring. With proper guidance from the group leader early in the game, this task favors flexibility in thinking, requires the student to make inferences, propose hypotheses about possible genotypes, and test these using proper breeding schedules. The participants must interpret the results of their simulated breeding schedules, analyze the phenotypic ratios of the offspring, and evaluate the validity of their hypothesis that suggested the adopted breeding schedule. It is important for the teacher to help students recognize the necessity of thinking flexibly about the possible genotypes that are represented by a particular phenotype and to propose a breeding schedule that yields the most information about the genotype at each step. The discussion is organized as follows. The group leader presents a hypothetical problem: a plant breeder wants to produce a plant with traits that are found disjunctively in two or more parent plants. The task is to breed the plants in such a way as to produce the desired progeny in the fewest possible breeding steps. After each step is proposed by the students, the leader informs the group of the phenotype ratios of the offspring. From these data, the students attempt to construct the genotype of the parent plants toward a better prediction of a more efficient breeding schedule. With careful thought, the students can minimize the number of moves needed to achieve the objective. They usually enjoy this task since they are competing against time rather than among themselves. There is usually a considerable amount of cooperation among college students when performing these tasks. Once the students get the idea of the game, they can create their own breeder's problems and assume the role of group leader. Several examples of these tasks are cited. I hope that the concept will be sufficiently well established after reading these examples that you will be able to create your own problems.

Problem 1. A breeder would like to produce an ornamental shrub with red flowers and leaves that are variegated (mottled). The plant should breed true. He has two kinds of plants to begin his project—one with white flowers and variegated leaves, and the other with red flowers and all green leaves. How can he most efficiently obtain his desired progeny? The phenotypes of the initial breeding stock are:

1. White flowers and mottled leaves
2. Red flowers and green leaves

The discussion leader has arranged that red flowers and all green leaves are simple dominant traits. The genotypes, unknown to the participants, are:

1. r r g g
2. R R G g

The participants have two choices for their first move. They can self-breed the parent plants or they can cross-breed the parent plants. The group leader should point out the two possibilities and let the group decide which move to make first.

If the participants self-breed the parent plants, they obtain offspring from parent 1 that are all identical to the parent. The offspring from self-breeding parent 2 yields a complex progeny. On the average, one expects to obtain 75 per cent of the progeny with red flowers and all green leaves, and 25 per cent with red flowers and mottled leaves. From this information, the pupils should be able to deduce that the desired progeny has been obtained from self-breeding parent 2. There will be a true-breeding plant with red flowers and mottled leaves in the progeny of the second parent. The evidence is as follows. Since parent plant 1 produced offspring identical to itself, its genotype must be homozygous for both alleles. The students can deduce that white flowers and mottled leaves are recessive traits since parent 2, which produced white-flowered and mottled-leaf off-spring, is a red-flowered, all green leaf parent. The only conclusion from both sets of data is that parent 2 is heterozygous and that self-breeding unmasked the recessive trait for mottled leaves. Therefore, one can immediately deduce with high assurance that the genotype of the desired plant obtained from the second parent plant is:

RR gg

It will, of course, breed true.

Now consider what would have been the product of cross-breeding the two initial plants. The offspring phenotype would be 50 per cent red-flowered, green-leaf plants and 50 per cent red-flowered, mottled-leaf plants, the students cannot know with assurance whether the red-flowered, mottled-leaf plant will breed true. They must make one more test to assess definitely the genotypes of the offspring. If they self-breed all of the red-flowered, mottled-leaf plants in the first generation, they obtain confirmation of the genotype since some (homozygous) breed true, whereas others (heterozygous) give variable offspring. It is obvious that the first strategy of self-breeding is the most efficient. The teacher should point out the differences in results from the two strategies. If the students are sufficiently informed, they can be asked to perform the critical analysis themselves. This will help prepare them for the second problem.

Problem 2. A plant breeder would like to produce a plant with pink flowers, hirsute (hairy) leaves, and winged petioles (petioles with a flattened blade-like projection). He has two plants with the following phenotypes:

1. White flower, smooth leaf with winged petiole
2. Pink flower, hirsute leaf without a winged petiole

The genotypes (not reported to the students) are characterized as follows:

The flower color is determined by a multiple allele.
R R and P P = deep red
R r and P P = light red
R r and p p, or r r and P P, or R r and p p = pink
r r and p p = white
Leaf hairs and petiole wings are each simple dominant traits.
H H or H h = hirsute leaf   W W or W w = winged leaf
h h = smooth leaf   w w = non-winged leaf

Assume the genotypes of the parent plants are:

1. r r p p h h W w
2. R R p p H H w w

If the students choose to self-breed the parents, they find that plant 1 breeds true on all traits except the winged petiole trait. On the average, 75 per cent have winged petioles and 25 per cent do not. Self-breeding plant 2 yields progeny with a phenotype identical to the parent. This strategy yields only one point of information; namely, that winged petiole is a recessive trait and that plant 1 is heterozygous for that trait. The students have no way of determining from this move what the genotype of the second plant is, other than that it is not heterozygous. If the students cross-breed the two plants on the first move, they find that the progeny all have pink flowers and hirsute leaves, but half are winged and the other half are not. If the class chooses to self-breed the pink-flowered, hirsute, winged-leaf plant they find that the flower color distributes as 75 per cent pink and 25 per cent white. These data are enough to indicate that flower color is not a simple dominant, single allele trait. The students can then select the progeny with the desired phenotype of pink flower, hirsute, winged-leaf and self-breed it. From this step, a true breeding strain is obtained, namely, the strain with genotype RR, pp, HH, WW. It is useful to begin by cross-breeding the parents since this provides the most information about genotype.

When the students go through several problems like this one in which the best strategy on the first move alternates between self-breeding and cross-breeding, they soon realize the necessity of flexible thinking. Students should be encouraged to think critically about their first move. The possible genotypes of the parents should be deduced from a critical consideration of the phenotypes of the plants. Based on this information, the students can plan their best first move strategy.

Problem 3. A more complicated problem can be created simply by increasing the number of traits to be considered and by increasing the number of plants in the initial breeding stock. Consider the problem of producing a plant that has pink flowers with fringed, bronze-colored leaves. The breeding stock consists of three plants with the following traits:

1. Red flowers and whole, fully green leaves
2. White flowers and whole, bronze-colored leaves
3. White flowers and fringed, fully green leaves

The genotypes, unknown by the pupils, are:

1. R R F F G G
2. r r F F g g
3. r r f f G G

Red flower is an incompletely dominant trait producing pink flowers when heterozygous. Fringed and bronze-colored leaves are each recessive traits.

If the students choose to self-breed the plants as the first step, they discover that all of the offspring are identical to the parent plant. This gives immediate information that all of the genotypes are homozygous.

If the students choose to cross-breed the plants, they find that for all possible crosses, the following results are obtained:

cross	*phenotypes*
1×2	Pink flowers and whole, fully green leaves
1×3	Pink flowers and whole, fully green leaves
2×3	White flowers and whole, fully green leaves

These data suggest that pink flowers are a hybrid effect, and that fringed and bronze-colored leaves are recessive traits in relation to whole and fully green leaf traits. When one examines the phenotypes of the parents, it becomes apparent that unless there are some complex multiple allele effects, parent 1 must be homozygous. The evidence for this is that the offspring from cross-breeding parent 1 with other plants produced only one kind of offspring identical to parent 1. Plant 3 must also be homozygous since it produced no recessive trait phenotypes when crossed with plants 1 or 2. By the same kind of argument, one can deduce that plant 2 is homozygous for all traits. If these assumptions are correct, the genotypes of the offspring are:

1 × 2	R r	F F	G g
1 × 3	R r	F f	G G
2 × 3	r r	F f	G g

Now, the task becomes one of planning a breeding schedule which unmasks the fringed-leaf, bronze-colored leaf trait in the presence of pink flowers. The students could suggest a strategy that uncovers each of the recessive traits in turn. It is obvious from the deduced genotypes that no single cross will yield in one step the desired offspring. If the offspring from cross 1×3 are bred with the offspring from cross 2×3, the fringed leaf characteristic is unmasked. If the offspring from cross 1×2 are bred with those from cross 2×3, the bronze-colored trait is unmasked. The progeny from either of these crosses can be self-bred to produce the desired offspring.

It is obvious, however, that these do not breed true since pink flower is a hybrid characteristic. The most efficient way to maintain a breeding stock is to grow parents of the following genotypes and cross-breed them whenever the desired offspring is wanted: R R, f f, g g, and r r, f f, g g. These are obtained in the offspring of the previously mentioned final self-breeding step. From this discussion, it is clear that in this problem it is better to begin with a cross-breeding step rather than a self-breeding step.

These problems are examples of the kind of discussion tasks teachers and students can prepare to stimulate problem-solving skill acquisition. Careful attention should be given to encourage widespread participation among all students. If several appear reticent to participate, you may want to break the class up into groups and allow the more retiring students to work on their own set of problems. The teacher needs to be sensitive to group dynamics and create the best combination of students to yield maximum interaction. Sometimes it is wise to include a mildly aggressive, yet understanding, student in the quiet students' group to help them gain some confidence in overt verbal expression. Obviously, the cognitive ability of the group determines how much autonomy they can endure in producing their own breeder's problems. Be alert to the kinds of strategies and cognitive skills used by the students. Some tend to use focussing techniques and arrange breeding schedules to carefully identify the genotypes one at a time. Others attempt to use scanning strategies where several traits are manipulated simultaneously. The group leader should help the participants recognize available strategies and encourage them to practice various ones. The effectiveness of each strategy should be analyzed in relation to the problem being solved. Ineffective strategies should be analyzed to determine the source of their failure in the context of a particular problem. The sources of problem-solving difficulties cited in

Chapter Two, should be kept in mind so that students with chronic problem-solving difficulties can be helped. The teacher should avoid the pitfall of generating the idea that a cook book approach to problem-solving is sufficient. Students should have the opportunity to develop creative problem-solving skills in pursuing science tasks such as those presented here.

REFERENCES

Adams, N. K. 1968. *The Physics and Chemistry of Surfaces* (New York, Dover Publications).

American Institute of Biological Sciences, Biological Sciences Curriculum Study 1963. *Biological Science: An Inquiry into Life* (New York, Harcourt, Brace & World); *Biological Science: Molecules to Man* (Boston, Houghton Mifflin); *BSCS Laboratory Blocks* (Boston, D.C. Heath); and *High School Biology: BSCS Green Version* (Chicago, Rand McNally).

Anderson, O. R. 1969. *Structure in Teaching: Theory and Analysis* (New York, Teachers College Press).

——— 1970a. "Experiments with the Role of Lipids in Cell-Membrane Permeability," *The American Biology Teacher* 32: 154-160.

——— 1970b. "Intracellular Digestion," *The American Biology Teacher* 32: 461-467.

——— 1971. *Quantitative Analysis of Structure in Teaching* (New York, Teachers College Press).

Ausubel, D. P. 1960. "The Use of Advance Organizers in the Learning and Retention of Meaningful Verbal Material," *Journal of Educational Psychology* 51: 267-272.

Berrill, N. J. 1966. *Biology in Action* (New York, Dodd, Mead).

Bloom, B. S. and L. J. Broder, 1950. *Problem-Solving Processes of College Students: An Exploratory Investigation* (Chicago, University of Chicago Press).

——— et al. 1966. *Taxonomy of Educational Objectives: The Classification of Educational Goals, Handbook I: Cognitive Domain* (New York, McKay).

Bourne, G. H. 1970. *Division of Labor in Cells* (New York, Academic Press).

Bruner, J. S. 1962. *The Process of Education* (Cambridge, Harvard University Press).

——— 1964. "The Course of Cognitive Growth," *American Psychologist* 19: 1-15.

——— 1967. *Toward a Theory of Instruction* (Cambridge, Belknap Press).

———, J. J. Goodnow, and G. A. Austin, 1956. *A Study of Thinking* (New York, Wiley).

Danielli, J. F. and H. Davson, 1935. "A Contribution to the Theory of Permeability of Thin Films," *Journal of Cellular and Comparative Physiology* 5: 495-507.

Dowdeswell, W. H. 1959. *Practical Animal Ecology* (London, Methuen).

Gagné, R. M. 1967a. *The Conditions of Learning* (New York, Holt, Rinehart and Winston).

——— 1967b. "Curriculum Research and the Promotion of Learning," in *Perspectives of Curriculum Evaluation,* B. O. Smith, ed. (Chicago, Rand McNally).

Giese, A. C. 1962. *Cell Physiology* (Philadelphia, W. B. Saunders).

Haskell, E. F. 1970. "Assembly of the Sciences into a Single Discipline," *Science Teacher Supplement* 37: 8-15.

Hilgard, E. R. and G. H. Bower, 1966. *Theories of Learning* (New York, Appleton-Century-Crofts).

Howland, J. L. 1968. *Introduction to Cell Physiology* (New York, Macmillan).

Katz, B. 1966. *Nerve, Muscle, and Synapse* (New York, McGraw-Hill).

Kavanau, J. L. 1965. *Structure and Function in Biological Membranes, Volumes 1 and 2* (San Francisco, Holden-Day).

Kormondy, E. J. 1969. *Concepts of Ecology* (Englewood Cliffs, New Jersey, Prentice-Hall).

Krathwohl, D. R. et al. 1964. *Taxonomy of Educational Objectives: The Classification of Educational Goals, Handbook II: Affective Domain* (New York, McKay).

Macan, T. T. and E. B. Worthington, 1951. *Life in Lakes and Rivers* (London, Collins).

Mager, R. F. 1962. *Preparing Instructional Objectives* (Palo Alto, Fearon).

Okey, J. R. and R. M. Gagné, 1970. "Revision of a Science Topic Using Evidence of Performance on Subordinate Skills," *Journal of Research in Science Teaching* 7: 321-325.

Schwab, J. J. 1963. *Biology Teachers Handbook* (New York, Wiley).

Shah, D. O. and J. H. Schulman, 1967. "Influence of Calcium, Cholesterol, and Unsaturation on Lecithin Monolayers," *Journal of Lipid Research* 8: 215-226.

Stein, W. D. 1968. "The Transport of Sugars," *British Medical Bulletin* 24: 146-149.

Trindade, A. L. 1970. "Structures in Science Teaching and Learning Outcomes," unpublished doctoral thesis, Teachers College, Columbia University.

Wallach, D. F. H. and P. H. Zahler, 1966. "Protein Conformation in Cellular Membranes," *Proceedings, National Academy of Science* 56: 1552-1559.

Different Paths
38888033851456